Great Taste No Pain!

Sherry Brescia

Great Taste No Pain!
October 2007 All rights reserved.

Cover design by Albert Agazaryan
Pencilpixel Graphics

ISBN 978-1-60461-843-3

Foreword

In 1988 I first became acquainted with the basic principles of food combining through Tony Robbins' book, Unlimited Power. It made a lot of sense, so I tried it out myself and was amazed at how much energy I had and how fantastic I felt after eating a "properly combined" meal. It excited me because I had hundreds of memories of being paralyzed with stomach pain after meals, unable to think of anything for hours except the rock in my stomach. Those days were over forever! Another thing that appealed to me was that I wasn't forced to give up any of the foods I loved... and *still* I had no stomach pain, no indigestion, no acid burps, and no more waking up in the middle of the night with the sweats "unable to go." The other thing I loved was that it was nearly impossible to gain weight eating this way.

I quickly became a disciple of this easy-to-understand, simple-to-follow healthy way of living. I told everyone who would listen about it. And being in a field where I was in constant contact with people who were 55 and older, nearly every one of my clients had stomach issues of one kind or another.

Without fail, everyone who tried what I shared with them experienced less pain and more energy whenever they followed the ridiculously simple guidelines. But absolutely no one I ever told about food combining ever lived by the principles like Sherry did.

It was September 1992 when Sherry made me dinner for the first time. We'd been dating for about a month. I was primarily vegetarian by then, but would still occasionally eat chicken, so she prepared chicken, rice and a beautiful salad. When I told her I'd eat either the chicken or the rice but not both at the same time, she couldn't imagine why I would say that. So, in about two minutes, I summarized a couple basic concepts of food combining and a few problems that might occur when you don't combine foods this way... (ie. when you eat like most other people).

Well, it must have made a lot of sense to her because she immediately began telling me about the problems she'd been experiencing for quite a number of years and about her 7 day hospital stay the year before. She told me the whole story... how she couldn't eat anything without agony, her family's history of stomach illnesses, her allergies, her crippling migraines, how she couldn't eat around people and before any gathering because of the embarrassment. She told me what her doctors said...and how they were absolutely no help at all. Her "IBS" literally affected every hour of her life.

And the thing she desperately wanted to know was if I thought she could get rid of her stomach pain and live a normal life even though she'd rarely had a pain-free day in the last 6 years. I told her that, while I wasn't an expert, even though she didn't eat junk food, her diet was acid creating and would cause anyone frequent pain, IBS or not. I told her that, while there were no guarantees, it was my opinion that if she ate in a way that required less stomach acid, her pain might very well go away.

So that night, her dinner was properly combined… and she had no pain! Before the evening was over, I wrote down the basic principles and laid out a two day diet plan to follow. The next day? No pain. It was that way the next day and the next day and the next. In fact, in the 15 years I've known Sherry (we were married in 1996!), I can count on one hand the number of times she's had a bad stomach ache. And in every case, it was because of eating foods that "didn't play nice" with one another.

Since that day in 1992, Sherry Brescia has become an expert not only in food combining and the effects of diet on health, but she's also become an expert in food preparation. Besides martial arts and her family, cooking is her biggest passion. She flat out loves to make great tasting foods. And she's great at it. So unlike any cookbook you've ever owned, where 98% of the recipes are hard to make, bland or just plain terrible tasting, every single recipe in this book is easy to make and *unbelievably* delicious. Frankly, cover to cover, the meals in this book will probably be the best food you've ever eaten in your life. And if you have major health issues, you will appreciate the effects these meals will have on your well being even more than the great taste.

You've made a wise choice in getting this book. I am fortunate that I get to eat Sherry's creations every day. I am living a food lover's dream life. And now that you have her finest recipes in your hands, you can live that dream, too. Congratulations, and welcome to our family!

Mike Brescia, President, Think Right Now, International
Author of the book, Today Is Your Day To Win

This book is dedicated to my parents.
Mom, you've always been my guiding light and my truest and dearest friend.
Dad, I wish I could have known you as an adult—it was hard to lose you as a child.
I hope I make you both proud.

Introduction

Welcome to your new life.

It has been said that out of all misfortune springs forth the seeds of opportunity.

For about six years until just after my 30th birthday, I experienced daily agonizing pain, but I overcame all my misery by making some very minor changes to my diet… those changes not only took away my pain, but they also gave me good health and energy like I'd never known before.

Whether you have frequent stomach pain, eat antacids like candy or are experiencing truly catastrophic illness, this book is your opportunity to experience the same health revolution in your life.

For most of my childhood, I had experienced terrible stomach pain when I ate. It seemed hit or miss, so I never attributed it to any specific foods. Then as a young adult in my early 20's, the problem escalated…I experienced stomach pain, bloating, gas and cramps after nearly every meal. During that time I also developed migraine headaches and allergies. I had pain or discomfort of some type every single day.

The medical community had one answer for me: drugs. I was prescribed an anti-spasmodic for IBS (irritable bowel syndrome), pain pills for the migraines and a steroidal inhaler for the allergies.

It just didn't seem right that a 28 year-old woman should have to take three medicines just to get through each day. After all, I took good care of myself—I ate what I thought were healthy foods (meat, pasta and vegetables), I did aerobics 3-5 times per week, didn't smoke or use illegal drugs, and drank wine only occasionally with meals. Why should I get this "life sentence" of needing daily medication just to survive?

Since the meds did nothing except mask my symptoms, and not very well at that, I continually searched for answers. The answer to my prayers came when I learned about proper food combining. Simply put, it's eating in the way that best allows the human body to comfortably digest any kind of food…even animal products. Once I began combining my foods properly, I was able to throw away all of my medications because all my symptoms disappeared instantly. No more stomach aches, no bloating, no

9

cramps, no gas, no migraines and no more allergies. And I have been symptom-free (and medication-free) ever since—for 15 years now.

Over these last 15 years, I've taken my love for cooking (and great food!) and the principles of food combining to create scrumptious, mouth-watering dishes that would satisfy even the pickiest eaters. That is what you now hold in your hands.

I began my new way of eating by adhering VERY strictly to the principles of proper food combining. I had no choice. My system was in tough shape and I needed to start feeling better immediately. If I hadn't, it was just a matter of time before I would be diagnosed with something worse and would need surgery and possibly even a colostomy.

Hopefully, you are not in as dire a situation as I was.

Whether you got this book to improve your health, eliminate pain, maintain your ideal weight or just to get recipes for some truly great tasting food, this is an important day in your life. And I am proud to be a part of it.

To learn the principles of food combining, why it works, how it works, and how simple it is to incorporate it into your life, read the downloadable guide, *How To End Stomach Pain Forever-Even If Your MD Says, "No Way"* that came with this book when you ordered it at www.GreatTasteNoPain.com.

To be able to follow these principles and stay pain-free no matter where you eat, look at the back of this book now and take out the *'Great Taste-No Pain Pocket Guide To Pain-Free Dining Out'* and put it in your wallet. Pull it out it whenever you need to be reminded how to properly combine your foods at a glance.

Here's to eating great and feeling great,

Sherry Brescia

Table of Contents

Breads and Breakfast Items   13

Condiments   27

Salads   39

Soups   49

Entrees   65

Vegetable Sides   119

Snacks and Entertaining   141

Desserts   151

Index – alphabetical   167

Index by category   177

Breads and Breakfast Items

Most recipes for quick breads (non-yeast breads such as zucchini bread, corn bread, pumpkin bread, banana bread and similar breads), muffins and pancakes contain mixtures of starches, proteins and sometimes fruit. Because of that, they are not easily digested. However, many people do enjoy a moist, tasty muffin or some pancakes for breakfast now and then. So for those people who "can't live without" these kinds of breads, most can eat them on a somewhat regular basis and still live completely free of stomach pain. Just remember that moderation is the key! All quick breads, muffins and breakfast pancakes ideally should be eaten under the following guidelines:

1) Have quick breads, muffins or pancakes for breakfast four times per month or less
2) Eat them alone on an empty stomach
3) Make sure your next two meals are at least 50% high water content foods to help cleanse your system

Blueberry Muffins   **Category: B**   **Makes: 6 jumbo
                                                                             muffins**

Hide any leftovers if you want them, because they will disappear quickly!

2 large eggs
1/2 cup canola oil
1 cup brown or raw sugar
1/2 teaspoons vanilla
Heaping 2 cups fresh or frozen and thawed blueberries
2 cups unbleached flour
1 teaspoon baking powder
1/2 teaspoon salt

Preheat oven to 350°.

In a large bowl, mix together the eggs, oil, sugar and vanilla. Stir in the blueberries.

Combine dry ingredients and fold carefully into moist ingredients until combined. (If batter appears too thick add a couple tablespoons of water to thin.)

Pour into lightly greased jumbo muffin tins. Bake for 30-35 minutes until a toothpick inserted in center comes out clean (except for blueberry stain!) and tops of muffins spring back when lightly touched.

Serve with:
Quick breads and muffins are best eaten alone for breakfast.

Breakfast Fritatta   **Category: C**   **Serves: 2-3**

A special breakfast for a weekend morning.

6 large eggs (preferably organic brown eggs)
1/3 cup milk or half-and-half
1/2 cup crumbled feta cheese
1/2 of a red bell pepper, diced
1/2 of a green bell pepper, diced
1/4 cup diced onion
1 cup broccoli florets, steamed until tender
1/2 cup white or baby Bella mushrooms, sliced
1/4 cup sliced black olives
Olive oil
Salt and pepper to taste
2 tablespoons grated Parmesan or Romano cheese for topping

Prepare all vegetables and have them ready.

In a deep mixing bowl, beat together eggs and milk or half-and-half. Stir in feta cheese.

Coat the bottom of a 10 inch skillet with olive oil and heat over medium heat. Add peppers and onions and sauté until they soften, about 5 minutes. Add broccoli, mushrooms and olives and sauté another 3 minutes.

Pour egg mixture evenly onto vegetables and cook, lifting up cooked egg around edge occasionally to let raw egg flow underneath, for about 3 minutes. Reduce heat to low and cook until underside is golden, about another 5 minutes.

The next step is up to you. If you want a "picture perfect" frittata, slide the frittata onto a plate, invert the pan onto the plate (using oven mitts) and flip the frittata over into the skillet. Or, if you don't care about being neat, break the frittata up into 5-6 manageable pieces with a spatula and flip them over individually in the pan. Continue cooking over low heat until the underside is golden, about 5 minutes. Sprinkle with Parmesan or Romano cheese and serve.

Variations:
- Substitute pitted kalamata olives for black olives
- Use whatever vegetables are your favorites—spinach, zucchini and escarole all work well
- Use shredded cheddar or Swiss cheese in place of the feta

<u>Serve with:</u>
Category A items of your choice

Breakfast Smoothies   **Category: Fruit**   **Serves: 2-3**

These are great for a light, tasty breakfast, as well as a refreshing snack in the middle of the day. They are also terrific as a "sauce" served over a fresh fruit salad.

4 cups fresh fruit of your choice
1 large banana
1 cup fruit juice
1 cup ice cubes

Put all ingredients into a blender; blend on high speed 1 minute until smooth and thoroughly mixed. If mixture is too thick, add fruit juice to desired consistency.

Great fresh fruit and juice combinations include:

- Mixed berries--strawberries, blueberries, blackberries and raspberries with berry juice
- Peaches, mangos, nectarines and pineapple with orange or pineapple juice
- Mixed melons—watermelon, cantaloupe and honeydew with mixed fruit juice
- Apples, pears and grapes with apple or cran-apple juice

Serve with:
These are made from fresh fruit, so they cannot be combined with any other food (except more fruit). They can be the first course of a larger breakfast or dinner, but wait 20 minutes for the smoothie to pass through the stomach before other foods are eaten.

Corn Bread   **Category: B**   **Serves: 6-8**

Moist and delicious.

1 1/4 cups flour
3/4 cup yellow corn meal
1/4 cup raw or brown sugar
2 teaspoons baking powder
1/4 teaspoon salt
1 cup milk
1/4 cup canola oil
1 egg, beaten

Preheat oven to 400°. Grease an 8" or 9" pan with butter or Earth Balance.

In medium bowl, combine dry ingredients and blend with a fork.

Stir in milk, oil and egg, mixing just until moistened. Pour batter into pan.

Bake for 20-25 minutes or until light golden brown and center springs back when lightly touched.

Serve warm with butter and maple syrup for breakfast, or with butter or salsa for dinner.

Serve with:
Quick breads and muffins are best eaten alone for breakfast.

Orange-Cranberry Bread   **Category: B**   **Serves: 8-10**

This is a nice addition to a brunch, or a special treat to make for a church bake sale.

2 cups unbleached flour
1 cup whole-wheat flour
1 cup sugar
1 tablespoon baking powder
1/2 teaspoon salt
1/2 teaspoon baking soda
1 cup orange juice
1/2 cup butter or Earth Balance, melted
2 eggs, beaten
1 1/2 cups fresh cranberries, chopped
2 teaspoons grated orange zest

Preheat oven to 350°. Grease and flour 9" x 5" loaf pan.

Combine dry ingredients. Combine juice, melted butter and eggs; add to dry ingredients and mix until moistened. Fold in cranberries and orange zest.

Pour batter into prepared pan. Bake for 70 minutes, or until toothpick inserted in center comes out clean.

Cool 5 minutes, remove from pan and continue cooling on rack. Serve with whipped butter.

Serve with:
Quick breads and muffins are best eaten alone for breakfast.

Nancy's Boston Brown Bread   **Category: B**   **Serves: 8-10**

My sister Nancy makes this bread for Christmas Day brunch every year, and it's positively scrumptious.

1 1/4 cups raisins
1 1/4 cups water
3 tablespoons shortening (I use Earth Balance shortening as a healthy alternative)
1 1/2 teaspoons baking soda

2 cups unbleached flour
1 cup sugar
2 eggs
1 teaspoon vanilla
1/2 cup chopped walnuts

Preheat oven to 350°.

Grease a 9"x 5" loaf pan.

Combine first four ingredients in a saucepan, bring to a boil over high heat, then remove from heat and cool.

Combine remaining ingredients with boiled mixture, pour into prepared pan and bake for 1 hour.

Cool 10 minutes, remove from pan and continue cooling on rack. Serve with whipped butter.

Serve with:
Quick breads and muffins are best eaten alone for breakfast.

Mom's Buttermilk Pancakes **Category: B** **Serves: 4-6**

These are delicious for breakfast, or even a simple supper.

2 cups unbleached flour
1 cup whole wheat flour
3 tablespoons sugar
3 teaspoons baking powder
1 1/2 teaspoons baking soda
3/4 teaspoon salt
3 cups buttermilk
1/2 cup milk
3 eggs
1/3 cup butter or Earth Balance, melted

In large mixing bowl, combine dry ingredients. In a separate small bowl, beat together buttermilk, milk, eggs and melted butter.

Heat a lightly oiled griddle or skillet over medium-high heat until a drop of water sizzles.

Add milk mixture to dry ingredients and stir just until moistened.

Drop batter by 1/2 cupfuls onto hot griddle. Fry until air bubbles form on tops of pancakes. Turn pancakes over and fry until brown.

Serve at once with butter and maple syrup, or keep warm in a 200° oven.

Serve with:
Pancakes are best eaten alone for breakfast or dinner.

Pumpkin-Apple Muffins   **Category: B**   **Makes: 9 jumbo muffins**

These are the perfect fall weather treat.

Muffins:
1 1/2 cups whole wheat flour
1 cup unbleached flour
1 tablespoon pumpkin pie spice
1 1/4 teaspoons baking powder
2 cups sugar
1 cup canned pumpkin
1/2 cup canola oil
2 eggs
1 cup peeled, cored and chopped apples
1 cup raisins
1/2 cup chopped walnuts or pecans

Topping:
1/2 cup brown sugar
2 tablespoons unbleached flour
1/2 teaspoon ground cinnamon
1/4 cup butter or Earth Balance

Preheat oven to 350°. Grease jumbo muffin tins. Combine flours, pie spice and baking powder in a medium mixing bowl. Stir together sugar, pumpkin, oil and eggs in a large bowl until well-combined. Add dry ingredients; stir until moistened. Fold in apples, raisins and walnuts. Spoon into muffin tins.

Prepare topping: Combine brown sugar, flour and cinnamon in a small bowl. Cut in butter with two forks or pastry blender until crumbly. Sprinkle on top of muffins. Bake for 35-40 minutes or until a wooden toothpick inserted in center comes out clean.

Serve with:
Quick breads and muffins are best eaten alone for breakfast.

Zucchini Bread   **Category: B**   **Makes: 2 loaves**

You can substitute raisins for the nuts if you wish, or use both.

3 eggs
1 cup oil
2 cups sugar
3 teaspoons vanilla
3 cups flour
1/4 teaspoon baking powder
1 teaspoon baking soda
1 teaspoon salt
3 teaspoons cinnamon
2 cups zucchini (peeled, raw, grated)
1 cup chopped nuts (optional)

Preheat oven to 325°. Lightly grease two loaf pans.

Beat eggs, oil, sugar and vanilla in a large mixing bowl. Sift dry ingredients together in a medium bowl and add to egg and oil mixture, mixing well. Fold in zucchini and nuts.

Pour into loaf pans and bake for 1 hour, or until a toothpick inserted in center comes out clean. Cool 10 minutes, then remove from pans and continue cooling on rack.

Serve with:
Quick breads and muffins are best eaten alone for breakfast.

Pumpkin Bread   **Category: B**   **Makes: 2 loaves**

The addition of the cornmeal gives this bread a dense, moist texture.

1 cup sugar
1 cup brown sugar
1 cup canola oil
3 eggs
2 cups canned pumpkin
2 cups unbleached flour
1 cup white or yellow cornmeal
1/2 teaspoon salt
1/2 teaspoon baking powder
1 teaspoon baking soda
1 teaspoon cloves
1 teaspoon cinnamon
2/3 cup raisins
2/3 cup walnuts

Preheat oven to 325°. In large mixing bowl, blend sugars and oil. Add egg and beat until light and fluffy. Blend in pumpkin.

Combine dry ingredients and blend into pumpkin mixture. Stir in raisins and walnuts. Divide between two greased and floured 9"x 5" loaf pans.

Bake 65 to 70 minutes, until toothpick inserted in center comes out clean. Let cool 10 minutes before removing from pans; continue cooling on rack.

Serve with:
Quick breads and muffins are best eaten alone for breakfast.

Condiments

Condiments have not been assigned a food category, since they are used in such small amounts and usually do not affect digestion of other foods.

The Best Thousand Island Salad Dressing   **Makes: 3 cups**

Once you make this yourself, you'll never go back to the bottled variety!

2 cups mayonnaise (I use canola mayonnaise)
1 hard-boiled egg, finely chopped
2 tablespoons Worcestershire sauce
1 1/2 teaspoons sugar
2 tablespoons cider vinegar
6 tablespoons sweet pickle relish
1/4 cup chopped black olives
1/4 cup diced red bell pepper

Combine all ingredients and chill.

Serve over mixed salad greens or as a dressing for sandwiches.

Spicy French Dressing   **Makes: 2-3/4 cups**

This also makes a great marinade for tough cuts of meat.

1 cup ketchup
3/4 cup olive oil
1/2 cup maple syrup
1/2 cup cider vinegar
1/2 teaspoon dry mustard
1/2 teaspoon ground ginger
1/2 teaspoon salt
1/2 teaspoon pepper
1 garlic clove, crushed

Whisk all ingredients together or blend in a blender on high speed for 30 seconds.

Coci Helen's Salad Dressing   **Makes: 3-1/2 cups**

"Coci" (pronounced chŭchi) means Aunt in Polish.   My Coci Helen made the best buttermilk dressing in the world.

2 cups mayonnaise
1 1/2 cups buttermilk
2 tablespoons white wine vinegar
1/2 cup chopped fresh chives
1/2 teaspoon sugar
Salt and pepper to taste

Whisk all ingredients together until smooth and well-combined. Chill.

Spoon over mixed green salad or use as a dip for vegetables.

Fresh Salsa   **Makes: 2-1/2 cups**

Why buy store-bought salsa when fresh tastes so much better and is so easy to make?

2 pounds ripe tomatoes (about 5 medium)
1-2 fresh jalapeno peppers (depending on your desired amount of "heat")
1/4 cup finely chopped white onion
1/2 cup fresh cilantro sprigs, chopped
3 cloves garlic, minced
1 teaspoon sugar
1 1/2 tablespoons fresh lime juice
Salt and pepper to taste

Seed tomatoes, dice into 1/4" pieces and place in bowl.

Seed and finely chop jalapenos, being careful not to touch your hands to your eyes. Add jalapenos to bowl and wash hands thoroughly with soap and water.

Add remaining ingredients to bowl; stir to combine.

Serve with tortilla chips, corn bread or corn fritters, or with your favorite Mexican dishes.

(This keeps for about 1 week in the refrigerator.)

Parsley Pesto   **Makes: 1/2 cup**

A different twist on the familiar basil pesto.

1 1/2 cups chopped fresh parsley
2 large cloves garlic, quartered
3 tablespoons Parmesan cheese
1 tablespoon white wine vinegar
1/4 cup olive oil
Salt and pepper to taste

Combine parsley, garlic, cheese and vinegar in a food processor. Process until finely chopped.

Keeping the motor running, pour oil through the food tube in a slow, steady stream.

Add salt and pepper and process just to combine.

This is a great addition to soups, stews, and pasta, or mix a spoonful with olive oil and use as a bread dip.

Basil Pesto   **Makes: 2/3 cup**

Easy and delicious.

40 fresh basil leaves
2 tablespoons pine nuts
2 large cloves garlic, chopped
1/4 cup Parmesan cheese
2 tablespoons Romano cheese
7 tablespoons olive oil
2 tablespoons hot water or broth
Salt and pepper to taste

Combine basil, pine nuts, garlic, cheeses and half of the oil in a food processor. Process until finely chopped.

Keeping the motor running, pour broth, salt and pepper through the food tube.

With motor still running, add remaining olive oil through the food tube and process until well-combined.

This is a great addition to soups, stews, and pasta, or mix a spoonful with olive oil and use as a bread dip.

Easy Homemade Pickles   **Makes: 3 quarts**

These are lighter and fresher tasting than your typical pickle.

10 unpeeled large cucumbers, very thinly sliced
3 cups water
3 cups white vinegar
2-1/2 cups sugar
1/4 cup salt
1/4 cup chopped fresh parsley
1 tablespoon celery seed
Pinch of white pepper
1 large onion, thinly sliced

In large mixing bowl, combine water, vinegar, sugar, salt, parsley, celery seeds and pepper.

Add cucumbers and onions, mix well to combine.

Divide into clean jars and cover tightly. Refrigerate at least 6 hours before serving.

Italian Butter (Bread Dipping Oil)   **Makes: 1 cup**

A tasty alternative to butter.

1 cup olive oil
1 tablespoon grated Parmesan or Romano cheese
1 tablespoon chopped fresh parsley
1 tablespoon chopped fresh basil leaves
1 teaspoon dried oregano
2-3 cloves garlic, pressed
1/2 teaspoon salt
1 teaspoon freshly ground black pepper

Combine all ingredients. Serve in shallow bowls or small plates with Italian, French or Sourdough bread slices.

Teriyaki Marinade   **Makes: 1-1/4 cups**

This is great on fish, steak or chicken.

1/2 cup tamari (soy sauce)
1/4 cup brown sugar
1/2 cup orange juice
3 cloves garlic, minced
1/2 teaspoon black pepper

Combine all ingredients in a small (non-metal) bowl. Pour over food and marinate for at least 3 hours.

Honey Mustard Vinaigrette   **Serves: 2 cups**

This can also be used as a basting sauce for grilling or broiling fish.

1/3 cup cider vinegar
1/3 cup Dijon mustard
1/3 cup honey
1 cup canola oil
Salt to taste

Whisk together all ingredients. Add salt to taste.

Cover and store in refrigerator.

Salads

Caesar Salad   **Category: A/C**   **Serves: 4-6**

I've experimented with many different versions of Caesar salad dressings, but this one is definitely the best.

1 very large head romaine lettuce, washed and torn into bite-sized pieces

Dressing:
3 cloves garlic, minced
3/4 cup mayonnaise
1 1/2 teaspoons anchovy paste
3 tablespoons Parmesan cheese
1/2 teaspoon Worcestershire sauce
1/2 teaspoon Dijon mustard
1 tablespoon fresh lemon juice
Salt and pepper to taste

Parmesan cheese for topping

Combine dressing ingredients and whisk until well combined.

Place lettuce in a very large bowl. Toss with dressing until well combined; top with additional Parmesan cheese and serve.

Note: This salad is perfectly combined. If serving with Category B items, you may need to omit cheese or substitute soy cheese for optimal digestion.

Serve with:
Category A items of your choice
Category C items of your choice

Fruit Salad   **Category: Fruit**   **Serves: 5-6 for breakfast, or 10-12 as a first course**

This is wonderful for breakfast, or as a colorful part of a summertime party buffet. If you can't find all the fruits I've listed, use whatever is in season. Note that frozen fruit does not work well in this recipe.

15 large fresh strawberries, rinsed, stems removed and quartered
2 cups fresh blueberries, rinsed and drained
2 cups fresh pineapple chunks
2 cups watermelon cubes
2 cups cantaloupe or honeydew melon cubes
3 kiwi fruit, peeled and sliced
2 cups grapes, removed from vine and rinsed
1 peach, rinsed and diced
1 pear, rinsed and diced
1 mango, peeled and diced
2 large bananas, peeled and sliced
1-4 oz. can pineapple juice
Raisins for garnish

Slice bananas, place in a bowl and pour pineapple juice over. Let them sit for 3 minutes then drain off juice. (This prevents them from turning brown.) Prepare other fruits and have them ready.

Using a very large, preferably clear glass or plastic bowl, put together salad in "layers": Put in a handful of strawberries, then blueberries, then pineapple, watermelon and cantaloupe, a few slices of kiwi, a handful of grapes, a few pieces of peach, pear and mango, and some banana slices. Keep repeating the process until all the fruit is used up. Sprinkle top with raisins. Serve immediately, or cover and chill up to 6 hours.

<u>Serve with:</u>
This is made entirely from fruit, so it cannot be combined with any other food (except more fruit). It can be the first course of a dinner, but wait 20 minutes for the salad to pass through the stomach before other foods are eaten.

Greek Salad   **Category: A/C**   **Serves: 4 generously**

This can be a meal in itself.

1 small head romaine lettuce, washed and torn into bite-sized pieces
1 cucumber, sliced
1 pint cherry tomatoes, halved
1 green bell pepper, sliced thin
1 small onion, sliced and separated into rings
1 cup kalamata olives
1 1/2 cups crumbled feta cheese

Greek Dressing:
1 cup olive oil
1/4 cup fresh lemon juice
2 teaspoons dried oregano
Salt and pepper to taste

Using a large platter or a very short and wide salad bowl, layer ingredients in order listed.

Whisk together dressing ingredients, and drizzle about 3/4 cup of dressing over salad. Serve and pass additional dressing as desired.

Note: This salad is perfectly combined. If serving with Category B items, you may need to omit cheese or substitute soy cheese for optimal digestion.

Serve with:
Category A items of your choice
Category C items of your choice

Italian Potato Salad   **Category: B**   **Serves: 3-4**

Simple and wonderful.

1 lb. new potatoes, skins left on
1/2 cup olive oil, plus more for drizzling
4 garlic cloves, minced
1/3 cup chopped fresh parsley
Salt and freshly ground pepper to taste

Boil potatoes in a large pot of salted water until tender; drain and cool slightly.

While potatoes are cooking, combine oil, garlic and parsley; set aside.

When potatoes are cool enough to handle, cut into bite-sized chunks. Place in a large bowl and toss with oil mixture. Season with salt and pepper to taste.   Drizzle with additional olive oil if salad appears to need moisture, as certain potatoes are more "dry" than others.

Let stand at room temperature for at least 1 hour before serving.

Serve with:
Category A items of your choice
Category B items of your choice

Spinach and Roasted Garlic Salad   Category: A/C   Serves: 4

This salad will make a spinach lover out of <u>anyone</u>!

12 garlic cloves, peeled
1/2 cup plus 2 tablespoons olive oil, divided
1 lb. baby spinach
1/2 cup pine nuts
1 tablespoon fresh lemon juice
1/2 cup Parmesan or Romano cheese, plus more for sprinkling
Salt and pepper to taste

Preheat oven to 375°.

Place garlic cloves in a small baking dish or foil packet, drizzle with 2 tablespoons olive oil and sprinkle with salt. Roast for 30-40 minutes until golden brown and soft when pierced with a sharp knife. Remove from oven, pour garlic and oil into a small bowl and mash garlic in oil with a fork. Set aside.

Meanwhile, place pine nuts on a baking sheet and toast in oven for 6-8 minutes until lightly browned. Set aside.

Place spinach in a very large bowl. Add garlic in oil and lemon juice and toss until well-coated. Drizzle remaining 1/2 cup olive oil over spinach and toss until well-mixed and spinach leaves start to wilt a bit. Add pine nuts, Parmesan or Romano cheese and salt and pepper and toss again.

Sprinkle with additional Parmesan or Romano and additional olive oil if desired and serve.

Note: This salad is perfectly combined. If serving with Category B items, you may need to omit cheese or substitute soy cheese for optimal digestion.

<u>Serve with:</u>
Category A items of your choice
Category C items of your choice

Diced Vegetable Salad Category: A/C Serves: 3

Try to make this up about half an hour before serving to allow flavors to meld, letting it sit at room temperature..

1 large cucumber, diced
1 large tomato, diced
1 red bell pepper, diced
1 green onion, sliced
1/4 cup minced fresh parsley
2 tablespoons olive oil
1 tablespoon fresh lemon juice
1 garlic clove, pressed
1/2 tsp dried oregano, crumbled
12 black olives, sliced
1 cup crumbled feta cheese
Salt and freshly ground black pepper to taste

Combine cucumber, tomato, bell pepper, green onion, parsley, oil, lemon juice, garlic, oregano, and olives in a large bowl. Add salt, pepper and feta; toss well.

Serve alone, on romaine lettuce leaves.

Note: This salad is perfectly combined. If serving with Category B items, you may need to omit cheese or substitute soy cheese for optimal digestion.

Serve with:
Category A items of your choice
Category C items of your choice

Tabouli   Category: B   Serves: 6-8

There are many variations of tabouli—some are mostly parsley and some mostly bulgur wheat. Mine is definitely heavier on the bulgur wheat.

1 cup bulgur wheat
1 1/2 cups boiling water
1 teaspoon salt
2 tablespoons fresh lemon juice
1/4 cup olive oil
3 cloves garlic, pressed
4 green onions, finely sliced
1/2 cup chopped fresh parsley
10 fresh mint leaves, finely chopped (or 1 tablespoon dried mint)
2 tomatoes, diced
1 cucumber, seeded and diced

Combine bulgur wheat and boiling water in a medium-sized bowl. Cover and let stand until bulgur is tender; at least 30 minutes.

In a large bowl, combine bulgur, salt, lemon juice, olive oil and garlic; mix thoroughly.

Stir in green onions, parsley, mint, tomatoes and cucumber. Let sit at least 30 minutes before serving.

Serve with:
Category A items of your choice
Category B items of your choice

Soups

Borscht   **Category: B**   **Serves: 4-6**

The Russian classic.

5-6 large fresh beets, peeled and sliced into matchstick-sized pieces
1 large onion, chopped
1/4 cup olive oil
2 celery stalks, sliced
3 carrots, peeled and sliced
1 red bell pepper, seeded and diced
2 cups shredded green cabbage
1 pkg. vegetarian burger crumbles (optional)
6-8 cups vegetable broth (use more if a more brothy soup is desired)
1 large or 2 small bay leaves
Pinch of thyme
Salt and pepper to taste
Sour cream for garnish (optional)

Have all vegetables prepared ahead of time.

Heat olive oil in a soup pot over medium heat and add onion. Sauté 5 minutes. Add celery and carrots and sauté 5 more minutes. Add red pepper and sauté a few minutes more. Add broth, beets, bay leaf, thyme, salt and pepper. Bring to a boil, reduce heat, cover and simmer for 30 minutes. Stir in cabbage and veggie burger crumbles (if using), return to a boil and simmer 15 more minutes or until all vegetables are tender. Remove bay leaf.

Serve in bowls with a dollop of sour cream in the middle for garnish if desired.

Serve with:
Rye bread (for optimal digestion, you may need to omit sour cream garnish)
Tossed salad
Category A items of your choice
Category B items of your choice (for optimal digestion, you may need to omit sour cream garnish)

Lentil Soup   **Category: B**   **Serves: 6**

This is perfect on a chilly winter night.

3 cups dry green lentils, rinsed and drained
7 cups vegetable broth
1 teaspoon salt
8 cloves garlic, crushed
1 large Vidalia onion, chopped
3 stalks celery, sliced
2 carrots, peeled and sliced
1 tablespoon chopped fresh basil (or 1 teaspoon dried basil)
1/2 teaspoon dried thyme leaves
1 teaspoon dried oregano
Pepper to taste
3 medium ripe tomatoes, diced (or 1-28oz. can diced tomatoes, undrained)

Place lentils, broth and salt in a Dutch oven or soup pot. Bring to a boil over high heat, reduce heat to low and simmer, partially covered, for 30 minutes. Add garlic, onion, celery, carrots, basil, thyme, oregano and pepper; simmer partially covered for an additional 15 minutes.

Stir in tomatoes and cook 10 minutes more, or until all vegetables and lentils are tender.

Serve with:
Italian bread
Category A items of your choice
Category B items of your choice

Black Bean Soup   **Category: B**   **Serves: 4-6**

I tried this dish at a local "honky-tonk" style restaurant and liked it so much, I had to duplicate it at home. If you can find fresh round loaves of bread in a bakery or grocery story, serve this in a whole-wheat bread bowl!

3 tablespoons olive oil
1 medium onion, chopped
2 carrots, diced
2 celery stalks, chopped
4 cloves garlic, minced
2 teaspoons ground cumin
1 teaspoon ground coriander
5 cups vegetable broth
2-15 oz. can black beans, rinsed and drained
Salt and pepper to taste
Sour cream for garnish (optional)

Heat the oil in a Dutch oven over medium heat. Sauté onion, carrots and celery about 5 minutes. Add garlic and sauté for 3 minutes more.

Add cumin and coriander and stir to combine. Add broth and beans. Bring to a boil, then reduce heat, cover and simmer for 20 minutes.

Top with a dollop of sour cream for garnish, if desired.

Note: For optimal digestion, you may need to omit the sour cream garnish.

Serve with:
Whole wheat bread
Tossed salad
Category A items of your choice
Category B items of your choice

Winter Vegetable Soup   **Category: B**   **Serves: 6-8**

I don't think that there's a vegetable that's NOT in this soup! You can substitute dried herbs for the fresh ones below, but try to resist, since the flavor is so much better with fresh.

1 can kidney beans, rinsed and drained
1 can Great Northern or cannellini beans, rinsed and drained
3 tablespoons olive oil
1 large Vidalia onion, chopped
4 cloves garlic, minced
1 1/2 cups diced fresh tomatoes (or use 1-15 oz. can diced tomatoes, undrained)
1/2 cup chopped fresh parsley
1/2 cup chopped fresh basil leaves
10 cups vegetable broth
2 potatoes, scrubbed and diced
3 large carrots, sliced
2 stalks celery, sliced
3 cups thinly sliced green or Savoy cabbage
2 small zucchini, scrubbed and diced
2 cups cauliflower florets
2 cups broccoli florets
1 cup fresh or frozen peas
Salt and pepper to taste
1/2 cup Parmesan or Romano cheese, plus more for garnish (optional)

Have all vegetables prepared before you start cooking, and making the soup will be a breeze.

Heat the oil over medium-high heat in a large soup pot or stock pot. Add onion and sauté 5 minutes. Add garlic and sauté another minute.

Add tomatoes, parsley, basil and broth. Bring to a boil, then reduce heat to low, cover and simmer for 15 minutes.

Add the potatoes, carrots, celery, cabbage and beans and simmer, covered, for 30 minutes more.

Add the zucchini, cauliflower, broccoli and peas and simmer, covered, for another 20 minutes or until all vegetables are tender.

Turn off the heat and allow soup to sit, covered, for 15 minutes for flavors to meld. Stir in cheese.

Top with additional Parmesan or Romano cheese, if desired.

Note: For optimal digestion, you may need to omit the cheese or substitute soy cheese.

<u>Serve with:</u>
Italian bread
Category A items of your choice
Category B items of your choice

Pasta E Fagioli   **Category: B**   **Serves: 6**

Good, old-fashioned Italian pasta and bean soup at its best. My husband Mike loves this dish.

3-15 oz. cans Great Northern or cannellini beans, rinsed and drained, divided
1/4 cup olive oil
1 large Vidalia onion, chopped
2 carrots, diced
2 stalks celery, sliced
4 cloves garlic, minced
1/2 cup chopped fresh parsley
1/4 cup chopped fresh basil leaves
8 cups vegetable broth
6 tablespoons tomato paste
Salt and pepper to taste
3 cups cooked small pasta, such as elbows, shells or bowties
1/2 cup grated Parmesan or Romano cheese, plus more for garnish (optional)

Drain and rinse one of the cans of beans and mash thoroughly or puree in a blender. Set aside. Drain and rinse other two cans of beans and set aside.

Heat oil in a Dutch oven or soup pot over medium heat and sauté onion 5 minutes. Add carrots, celery, garlic, parsley and basil and cook another 8-10 minutes. Stir in broth, mashed or pureed beans, whole beans and tomato paste. Bring to a boil over high heat, then reduce heat, cover and simmer for 30 minutes or until carrots and celery are tender.

Stir in pasta and cook just long enough to heat pasta through, about 2-3 minutes. If soup seems too thick, add a little extra water or vegetable broth. Stir in cheese.

Top with additional Parmesan or Romano cheese if desired.

Variation: To prevent pasta from getting too soft if there are leftovers, instead of adding pasta to soup while cooking, you can keep them separate and just add pasta to individual bowls as the soup is served.

Note: For optimal digestion, you may need to omit the cheese or substitute soy cheese.

Serve with:
Warm garlic bread
Tossed salad
Category A items of your choice
Category B items of your choice

Corn Chowder   **Category: B**   **Serves: 4**

This was always one of my daughter Danielle's favorite meals when she was small.

1 large onion, chopped
2 cloves garlic, chopped
1 large potato, chopped
2 stalks celery, sliced
1 green bell pepper, seeded and diced
2 tablespoons olive oil
2 tablespoons butter or Earth Balance
2 1/2 cups vegetable broth
Salt and pepper to taste
1 1/4 cups milk or rice milk
2 1/2 cups fresh or frozen corn kernels
Pinch of dried sage
Grated cheddar cheese for garnish (optional)

Heat oil and butter in a Dutch oven or soup pot over medium-high heat. Add onion, garlic, potato, celery and pepper and heat to sizzling. Cover, reduce heat to low and cook the vegetables for 10 minutes.

Add the broth, season with salt and pepper to taste, and bring to a boil. Reduce heat to low, cover and simmer for 15 minutes. Stir in the milk, corn and pinch of sage; simmer for 5 more minutes. Serve hot, topped with grated cheddar cheese as a garnish if desired.

Note: For optimal digestion, you may need to omit the cheese or substitute soy cheese AND use rice milk instead of cow's milk.

Serve with:
French bread
Category A items of your choice
Category B items of your choice

Minestrone Soup   **Category: B**   **Serves: 6**

There are many variations to this recipe, but this is the one that most people ask me to make time and time again.

6 cups vegetable broth
3 tablespoons olive oil
1 large onion, chopped
1 leek, white part only, thinly sliced, rings separated, soaked in cold water to remove sand and drained
3 carrots, sliced
2 stalks celery, sliced
4 cloves garlic, pressed
2 large potatoes, scrubbed and diced
1 1/2 cups fresh green beans, trimmed and sliced into bite-sized pieces
1 bay leaf
1/4 teaspoon thyme
1 cup fresh or frozen peas
3 small zucchini, scrubbed and diced
3 medium tomatoes, chopped
1-15 oz. can cannellini beans, rinsed and drained
3 tablespoons basil pesto (for homemade, see recipe on p. 34)
1/2 cup Parmesan cheese, plus more for garnish (optional)

In a Dutch oven or large soup pot, heat olive oil over medium-high heat. Add onion and leek and sauté for 5 minutes. Add carrots, celery and garlic and cook over medium heat for another 5 minutes. Add potatoes and green beans and cook for 3 minutes more.

Add broth, bay leaf and thyme and stir well. Bring to a boil, reduce heat, cover and simmer for 15 minutes.

Add peas (if using fresh) and tomatoes and simmer 10 minutes more. Stir in zucchini, frozen peas (if using) and cannellini beans and simmer for 8 minutes or until all vegetables are tender. Remove bay leaf.

Remove from heat, stir in pesto and cheese and top with additional cheese as a garnish.

Note: For optimal digestion, you may need to omit the cheese or substitute soy cheese.

Serve with:
Italian bread
Simple green salad with oil and vinegar
Category A items of your choice
Category B items of your choice

Asparagus Soup   **Category: A**   **Serves: 4**

When my son Mickey was very little and couldn't say "asparagus," he would simply ask me to make "green soup." He still loves it but now asks for it by name!

1 1/2 lbs. fresh asparagus
4 tablespoons butter or Earth Balance, divided
6 shallots, sliced or 1 large onion, diced
1 tablespoon unbleached flour
4 cups vegetable broth
1/2 cup milk, light cream, rice milk or soy milk
Salt and pepper to taste

Trim the asparagus stalks to remove tough bottom portion. Cut the tops off of half of the asparagus and set aside. Cut the remaining asparagus into 2" pieces.

In Dutch oven or soup pot, melt 2 tablespoons butter over medium heat. Add shallots or onion and sauté 5 minutes, stirring occasionally. Add asparagus pieces and fry over low heat for 2 minutes. Stir in flour and cook for 1 minute more. Stir in broth, bring to a boil, then simmer partially covered over low heat for 15-20 minutes.

Cool soup slightly, then puree in batches in blender or food processor. Return soup to pan and reheat gently over low heat. While soup heats, melt remaining 2 tablespoons butter in a small skillet. Sauté remaining asparagus tips until tender, about 4-5 minutes.

Add milk or cream to soup, season with salt and pepper to taste, and stir in sautéed asparagus tips.

Note: For optimal digestion, you may need to use rice milk or soy milk instead of cow's milk or cream.

Serve with:
Sourdough bread
Category A items of your choice
Category B items of your choice

Cream of Mushroom Soup   **Category: B**   **Serves: 4**

The addition of the tiny pasta shapes to this soup makes it truly unique.

2 teaspoons butter or Earth Balance
1 onion, finely chopped
3/4 pound mushrooms, finely chopped
1 tablespoon all purpose flour
2 1/2 cups vegetable broth
1 1/4 cups milk, rice milk or soy milk
Salt and freshly ground black pepper
1/2 cup cooked tiny pasta shapes (such as pastina, orzo or ditalini)
Pinch freshly grated nutmeg

Melt the butter in a Dutch oven or large sauce pan over medium heat, and sauté onion for about 3 minutes until softened. Add the chopped mushrooms, cover and cook for a further 5 minutes.

Stir in flour, then gradually add broth and milk, stirring well after each addition. Bring to a boil, then reduce heat to low, cover and simmer for 15-20 minutes, stirring occasionally.

Season to taste with salt and freshly ground pepper. Stir in pasta and nutmeg. Cook for a final 2-3 minutes and serve.

Note: For optimal digestion, you may need to use rice milk or soy milk instead of cow's milk.

Serve with:
Tossed salad
Italian bread
Category A items of your choice
Category B items of your choice

Tomato Soup With Basil   **Category: A**   **Serves: 4**

You can "take the easy way out" and just dice the tomatoes without peeling, and it will still be delicious!

3 large ripe tomatoes
2 tablespoons olive oil
1 medium onion, finely chopped
1 clove garlic, crushed
1 small red bell pepper, finely chopped
4 cups vegetable broth
3 tablespoons tomato paste
Salt and pepper to taste
1 teaspoon sugar
1/4 cup chopped fresh basil leaves (or 1 1/2 teaspoons dried)
Fresh basil leaves for garnish
Grated Parmesan or Romano cheese for garnish (optional)

Cut a small cross in the top of each tomato. Place in a bowl and cover with boiling water for about 2 minutes; drain and cool. Peel skin downward from the cross and discard. Roughly chop flesh.

Heat oil in a Dutch oven or large soup pot over medium heat. Add onion, garlic and red pepper; cook, stirring, for about 10 minutes or until all ingredients are soft. Add tomatoes and cook for another 10 minutes. Add the broth, tomato paste, salt, pepper and sugar. Cover and simmer for 15 minutes. Remove from heat, stir in basil and allow to cool slightly.

Process soup in batches in a food processor or blender until smooth. Return the mixture to the pan and reheat over low heat. Top with fresh basil leaves and grated Parmesan or Romano cheese if desired.

Serve with:
Italian bread (for optimal digestion, you may need to omit cheese garnish or substitute soy cheese)
Category A items of your choice
Category B items of your choice (for optimal digestion, you may need to omit cheese garnish or substitute soy cheese)

Carrot And Cilantro Soup   **Category: B**   **Serves: 6-8**

Another restaurant-inspired idea of mine. The original version was made with basil, but the cilantro and coriander combination really makes it something special.

2 tablespoons olive oil
3 tablespoons butter or Earth Balance
1 large Vidalia onion, chopped
3 stalks celery, sliced
2 medium potatoes, chopped
2 pounds carrots, cut into 1 1/2" chunks
6 cups vegetable broth
3 teaspoons ground coriander
1/4 cup chopped fresh cilantro (or 1 tablespoon dried)
Salt and freshly ground black pepper to taste

Heat oil and butter in a Dutch oven or soup pot over medium heat. Sauté onion for 3-4 minutes until slightly softened. Add celery and potatoes to the onion in the pan, cook for a few minutes and then add the carrots. Sauté for 3-4 minutes, stirring frequently. Cover, reduce heat to low and "sweat" vegetables for 10 minutes. Gently shake the pan or stir occasionally so the vegetables do not stick to the bottom.

Add the broth, bring to a boil and then cover and simmer for 10 minutes, or until the carrots and potato are tender. Remove from heat and cool slightly.

Process the soup in batches in a food processor or blender until smooth. Return soup to pan, stir in coriander, cilantro and salt and pepper to taste. Reheat over low heat and serve immediately.

Serve with:
French bread
Category A items of your choice
Category B items of your choice

Entrees

Sherry Brescia's Outrageously Delicious Spaghetti Sauce   **Makes: 8 quarts**
Category: A

I created this sauce with my husband Mike's help. He suggested the key ingredient—eggplant.

4 - 28 oz. cans crushed tomatoes
4 - 12 oz. cans tomato paste
1 large Vidalia or Spanish onion, chopped
1 head garlic, peeled and minced
1 medium eggplant, washed and diced
4 cups loosely packed fresh basil leaves
2 tablespoons dried oregano
1 tablespoon sugar
1/2 cup dry red wine
2 cups olive oil, divided
Water as needed for desired consistency
1 cup grated Parmesan or Romano cheese

In large stockpot, sauté onion in 3/4 cup olive oil for 5 minutes; add garlic and sauté another 2-3 minutes. Add eggplant and another 1/4 cup olive oil; sauté 4-5 minutes.

Stir in tomato paste, crushed tomatoes, 1/2 cup olive oil, wine and enough water to desired consistency. (I usually add about 2 cups.)

Place basil in large bowl or glass measuring cup; snip with kitchen shears into small pieces and stir into sauce. Add oregano and sugar.

Simmer 4 hours, adding splashes of remaining 1/2 cup olive oil periodically. When done, stir in Parmesan or Romano cheese.

Use as a sauce over pasta, for lasagna or for Eggplant Parmesan.

Bowties and Broccoli   **Category: B**   **Serves: 4-6**

Without exception, whenever we have a family "potluck" party, everyone always asks me to bring this dish!

1-1 lb. box of bowtie pasta (or any pasta shapes of your choice)
1 1/2 cups olive oil, divided
2 bunches broccoli, broken into florets
8 cloves garlic, minced
1 cup chopped fresh parsley
1 cup grated Parmesan or Romano cheese
Garlic salt and pepper to taste

Cook pasta in a large soup kettle in a generous amount of salted water, to which 1 tablespoon of olive oil has been added.

While pasta cooks, steam broccoli until just tender; drain and set aside.

Sauté garlic in 1/2 cup olive oil until fragrant but not browned; remove from heat and set aside.

When pasta is done, drain and return to soup pot. Stir in garlic and oil from sauté pan, parsley, grated cheese, broccoli and remaining olive oil until well mixed. Add garlic salt and pepper to taste. If mixture seems too dry, add a bit more olive oil.

Sprinkle additional cheese on top, if desired, and serve.

Note: For optimal digestion, you may need to omit the cheese or substitute soy cheese.

Serve with:
Tossed salad
Category A items of your choice
Category B items of your choice

Sundried Tomato Pasta   **Category: B**   **Serves: 4-6**

This is delicious hot or at room temperature.

1-1 lb. box of pasta spirals (or any pasta shapes of your choice)
1 cup olive oil
6 plum tomatoes, diced
1-8oz. jar sliced or julienne sundried tomatoes in oil, undrained
2/3 cup chopped fresh basil leaves
1 tablespoon dried oregano
1 cup grated Parmesan or Romano cheese, plus additional for garnish
Salt and pepper to taste

Cook pasta in a large soup kettle in a generous amount of salted water, to which 1 tablespoon of olive oil has been added.

When pasta is done, drain and return to soup pot. Stir in sundried tomatoes, basil, oregano, grated cheese, fresh tomatoes and olive oil until well mixed. Add salt and pepper to taste. If mixture seems too dry, add a bit more olive oil.

Sprinkle additional cheese on top, if desired, and serve.

Note: For optimal digestion, you may need to omit the cheese or substitute soy cheese.

Serve with:
Tossed salad
Category A items of your choice
Category B items of your choice

Broccoli & Swiss Cheese Quiche   **Category: C**   **Serves: 6-8**

Perfect for dinner, brunch or a picnic lunch.

7 large eggs
1/2 cup light cream
1/2 lb. Swiss cheese, cubed
2 bunches broccoli, broken into florets
1 medium onion, chopped
3 tablespoons butter
1/2 teaspoon salt
1/4 teaspoon pepper
1 cup mushrooms, sliced
1 unbaked pie shell (for homemade crust, see recipe on p. 157)

Preheat oven to 425°. Roll out pie shell and place in a quiche dish or deep pie pan.

Steam broccoli until just tender; drain. Sauté onion in butter until translucent (about 5 minutes); add mushrooms and sauté 3 minutes more.

Beat eggs in a large bowl. Stir in cream, cheese, broccoli, onion and mushrooms (with butter from sauté pan), salt and pepper. Pour into pie shell.

Bake at 425° for 15 minutes, then 375° for 40-50 minutes or until done. Quiche is done when it is firm in the center, springs back when touched lightly, and knife inserted near center comes out clean.

Note: For optimal digestion, you may need to omit the pie crust. (Be sure to grease the pan before pouring in egg mixture.)

Serve with:
Tossed salad
Summer Squash Sauté
Category A items of your choice

Spinach & Feta Cheese Quiche   **Category: C**   **Serves: 6-8**

The addition of feta cheese makes this quiche rich and tasty.

7 large eggs
1/2 cup light cream
1/2 lb. feta cheese, crumbled
1 lb. spinach
3 cloves garlic, minced
3 tablespoons olive oil
1/2 teaspoon garlic salt
1/4 teaspoon pepper
1 unbaked pie shell (for homemade crust, see recipe on p. 157)

Preheat oven to 425°. Roll out pie shell and place in a quiche dish or deep pie pan.

Steam spinach just until wilted; drain, squeeze dry and chop. Sauté garlic in olive oil until fragrant but not browned; remove from heat.

Beat eggs in a large bowl. Stir in cream, cheese, spinach, garlic (with oil from sauté pan), garlic salt and pepper. Pour into pie shell.

Bake at 425° for 15 minutes, then 375° for 40-50 minutes or until done. Quiche is done when it is firm in the center, springs back when touched lightly, and knife inserted near center comes out clean.

Note: For optimal digestion, you may need to omit the pie crust. (Be sure to grease the pan before pouring in egg mixture.)

Serve with:
Tossed salad
Category A items of your choice

Spanakopita   **Category: B**   **Serves: 5-6**

I don't know what the literal translation is for the word "Spanakopita," but I would say it means "heaven on earth" because that's what these taste like!

2 lbs. spinach
1/2 lb. feta cheese, crumbled
1-16oz. carton ricotta cheese
4 cloves garlic, minced
3 green onions, thinly sliced
2 tablespoons olive oil
1/2 cup chopped fresh parsley
1 tsp. garlic salt
Olive oil as needed
1 pkg. Greek phyllo dough (usually found in the frozen food section of grocery stores); thawed

Preheat oven to 350°.

Make the filling:
Steam spinach just until wilted; drain, squeeze dry and chop. Sauté garlic and green onions in olive oil until garlic is fragrant but not browned; remove from heat. Combine spinach, feta, ricotta, garlic, onions and oil from sauté pan, parsley and garlic salt in a large mixing bowl; stir until well mixed.

Assemble the spanakopita:
Note: Phyllo dough is delicious and wonderfully crisp and flaky, but must be kept from getting too much air, as it dries out very quickly. Have ready the prepared filling, a small bowl of olive oil (about 3/4 cup), a pastry brush, kitchen shears and a damp kitchen towel before you get started.

Unwrap phyllo dough and lay flat on work surface; cut in half the long way with kitchen shears and quickly cover with a damp kitchen towel.

Peel back just enough kitchen towel so you can grab a stack of about 4-5 half-sheets of dough; lay them flat in front of you in a stack and quickly cover the remaining dough back up. Brush the top sheet in the stack with olive oil.

Place about 1/2 cup of filling onto one of the corners of dough closest to you. Gently fold edge of dough and filling over diagonally to form a triangle. Fold dough and filling triangle straight up, then diagonally, then straight up again, then diagonally, retaining triangle shape throughout (like a flag being folded by the military or a paper football being folded by a middle school boy).

Fold down any remaining dough and tuck underneath the triangle. Brush underside with olive oil, place onto a cookie sheet and brush top and sides with olive oil.

Repeat the above process until filling is gone.

Bake at 350° for about 30 minutes or until golden brown and crisp.

Note: For optimal digestion, you may need to omit the cheese or substitute soy cheese.

Serve with:
A simple green salad with oil and vinegar
Category A items of your choice

Eggplant Parmesan   **Category: B**   **Serves: 10-12**

Perfect for a dinner party.

1 batch Sherry Brescia's Outrageously Delicious Spaghetti Sauce (recipe on p. 67) or 3 jars store-bought
spaghetti sauce
5 large eggplants
4 eggs, beaten
2-3 cups Italian breadcrumbs
Olive oil for frying
2 1/2 cups grated Parmesan cheese
2 cups shredded mozzarella cheese
Dried basil and oregano for sprinkling

Preheat oven to 350°.

Wash and slice eggplants into 1/2 inch rounds. Pour enough olive oil into a large skillet so that there is a
1/4 inch covering on the bottom. Heat over medium heat until a drop of water sizzles.

Dip eggplant rounds in beaten egg, then press both sides into breadcrumbs to coat lightly. Fry in olive
oil until browned on both sides; drain on paper towels. Continue the process until all of the eggplant
rounds are fried, adding additional olive oil to the skillet as needed.

Lightly coat bottom of a 13" x 9" baking pan with olive oil. Place a layer of eggplant over oil,
generously cover with spaghetti sauce, and sprinkle with basil and oregano. Sprinkle with 1/2 cup each
of Parmesan and mozzarella. Repeat process three times (eggplant, sauce, basil, oregano, cheese) to
form three more layers. For top (5th) layer, place eggplant rounds over cheese from previous layer,
cover generously with spaghetti sauce, and sprinkle with final 1/2 cup Parmesan cheese.

Cover and bake at 350° for 1 1/4 hours or until hot all the way through and bubbly. Top with additional
spaghetti sauce, if desired.

Note: For optimal digestion, you may need to bake the eggplant in a 375° oven for 12-15 minutes instead of breading and frying; or omit the cheese; or substitute soy cheese.

<u>Serve with:</u>
Tossed salad
Category A items of your choice
Category B items of your choice (for optimal digestion, you may need to omit the cheese or substitute soy cheese)

Ratatouille   **Category: A**   **Serves: 4-6**

This is especially delicious when made with the freshest summer vegetables in season.

1/4 cup olive oil
5 cloves garlic, minced
1 large Vidalia onion, diced
1 bay leaf
1 large eggplant, washed and cubed
1 teaspoon salt
1/4 cup chopped fresh basil leaves (or 2 teaspoons dried)
2 teaspoons dried oregano
1 teaspoon rosemary leaves
2 small zucchini, washed and cubed
2 small yellow summer squash, washed and cubed
1 red and 1 green bell pepper, seeded and chopped
1-28 oz. can diced tomatoes
1/2 cup dry red wine
8 oz. mushrooms, sliced
1/4 cup fresh minced parsley
Grated Parmesan or Romano cheese for garnish (optional)

Heat olive oil in a saucepot or Dutch oven. Add onion, garlic and bay leaf and sauté over medium heat for 5 minutes.

Add eggplant, salt, basil, oregano and rosemary; cover and cook over medium heat for 10 minutes, stirring occasionally.

Add zucchini, yellow squash, peppers tomatoes and wine; cover and simmer over low heat for 10 minutes. Add mushrooms and parsley and simmer 5 minutes more, or until all vegetables are tender. Remove bay leaf.

Top with grated Parmesan or Romano cheese, if desired.

<u>Serve with:</u>
Sourdough bread or Italian bread (for optimal digestion, you may need to omit the cheese garnish)
Category A items of your choice
Category B items of your choice (for optimal digestion, you may need to omit the cheese garnish)

Corn Fritters   **Category: B**   **Serves: 3-4**

These are scrumptious for breakfast or dinner.

3/4 cup cornmeal
3/4 cup unbleached flour
2 teaspoons baking powder
Salt and pepper to taste
1 1/2 teaspoons sugar
1/2 teaspoon ground cumin
1/2 cup milk or rice milk
2 eggs
1 1/2 cups corn kernels, fresh, canned or frozen and thawed

Combine cornmeal, flour, baking powder, salt, pepper, sugar and cumin in a large bowl.

Beat together the milk and eggs and stir into dry ingredients until well-combined. Stir in corn kernels.

Drop by 1/4 cupfuls onto hot, greased skillet or griddle. Cook over medium heat, turning once, until browned on both sides.

Serve with maple syrup for breakfast or tomato salsa for dinner.

Note: For optimal digestion, you may need to use rice milk instead of cow's milk, and an egg replacer—4 tablespoons of cornstarch beaten with 4 tablespoons of water—instead of eggs.

Serve with:
Fresh Salsa
Category A items of your choice
Category B items of your choice

Lasagna with Vegetables **Category: B** **Serves: 10-12**

Making homemade lasagna sometimes scares busy cooks because it takes a little time. It's definitely worth the effort, but I've also included some frozen/canned options for the vegetables as short-cuts if you're short on time.

1 batch Sherry Brescia's Outrageously Delicious Spaghetti Sauce (recipe on p. 67) or 3 jars store-bought spaghetti sauce
1-1 lb. box lasagna noodles
1 lb. spinach
1 large bunch broccoli, broken into florets
8 oz. mushrooms, sliced
5 tablespoons olive oil, divided
2 red bell peppers, chopped
2 small zucchini, sliced
16 oz. carton ricotta cheese
1 lb. mozzarella cheese, shredded
1 1/2 cups grated Parmesan or Romano cheese; plus more for sprinkling on top of lasagna
Dried basil and oregano for sprinkling

Preheat oven to 350°. Prepare noodles and all vegetables first and assembling the lasagna will be a breeze:

- Precook lasagna noodles according to package directions; drain and rinse with cool water.

- Steam spinach until just wilted; squeeze dry and chop. (Or use frozen chopped spinach, thawed and squeezed dry.)

- Steam broccoli florets until just tender; set aside. (Or use frozen chopped broccoli, thawed.)

- Sauté mushrooms in 1 tablespoon olive oil for 3 minutes; set aside. (Or use canned mushrooms, drained.)
- Sauté peppers in 1 tablespoon olive oil for 5 minutes; set aside.

- Sauté zucchini in remaining 3 tablespoons olive oil for 5 minutes or just until slightly tender; set aside.

Now assemble the lasagna:

Cover bottom of a 13"x 9" baking pan with spaghetti sauce. Place a single layer of noodles on top of sauce. Sprinkle all of spinach over noodles; drop 1/4 of the ricotta on top of spinach in dollops; sprinkle with 1/4 of the mozzarella and Parmesan/Romano cheeses, sprinkle generously with basil and oregano, then cover with a layer of sauce.

Repeat process with the broccoli next: Place a layer of noodles down, cover with all of broccoli; drop 1/4 of the ricotta on top of broccoli in dollops; sprinkle with 1/4 of the mozzarella and Parmesan/Romano cheeses, sprinkle generously with basil and oregano, then cover with a layer of sauce.

Repeat the above process creating two more layers—one with the red peppers and mushrooms, and the other with the zucchini.

Cover everything with a final layer of lasagna noodles, top with a generous layer of sauce, and sprinkle top with Parmesan or Romano cheese.

 Bake covered at 350° for 1 hour and 15 minutes, or until lasagna is hot and bubbly throughout. Top with additional sauce if desired.

This dish can be made ahead and refrigerated or frozen. If refrigerated, bring to room temperature before baking. If frozen, bake without thawing for 2 1/2 hours or until hot.

Note: For optimal digestion, you may need to omit the cheese or substitute soy cheese.

Serve with:
Tossed salad
Category A items of your choice
Category B items of your choice

Lasagna with Meat   **Category: B**   **Serves: 10-12**

I use veggie burger crumbles and vegetarian Italian sausage in this recipe. You can use ground beef and hot sausage if you desire, but know that it's meat & starch—a serious mis-combination.

1 batch Sherry Brescia's Outrageously Delicious Spaghetti Sauce (recipe on p. 67) or 3 jars store-bought spaghetti sauce
1-1 lb. box lasagna noodles
1-12 oz. package frozen veggie burger crumbles (I recommend Morning Star Farms), thawed
1 1/2 packages (about 1 lb.) frozen veggie Italian sausage (I recommend Boca brand)
3 tablespoons olive oil
8 hard boiled eggs, sliced and divided into 4 groups of 2 eggs each
16 oz. carton ricotta cheese
1 lb. mozzarella cheese, shredded
1 1/2 cups grated Parmesan or Romano cheese; plus more for sprinkling on top of lasagna
Dried basil and oregano for sprinkling

Preheat oven to 350°.

Prepare noodles and all filling ingredients first and assembling the lasagna will be a breeze:

- Precook lasagna noodles according to package directions; drain and rinse with cool water.

- Drain veggie burger crumbles if necessary and set aside.

- Place veggie sausages in a small amount of water in a skillet over medium heat. Bring to a boil, reduce heat to low and simmer 10 minutes. Drain water, add olive oil and brown sausages over medium low heat. Cool and cut into thin slices.

Now assemble the lasagna:

Cover bottom of a 13"x 9" baking pan with spaghetti sauce. Place a single layer of noodles on top of sauce. Cover with about 1/4 each of burger crumbles and sausage, layer 2 of the sliced eggs on top of veggie meats. Drop 1/4 of the ricotta on top of eggs in dollops; sprinkle with 1/4 of the mozzarella and Parmesan/Romano cheeses, sprinkle generously with basil and oregano, then cover with a layer of sauce.

Repeat the above process creating three more layers.

Cover everything with a final layer of lasagna noodles, top with a generous layer of sauce, and sprinkle top with Parmesan or Romano cheese.

 Bake covered at 350° for 1 hour and 15 minutes, or until lasagna is hot and bubbly throughout. Top with additional sauce if desired.

This dish can be made ahead and refrigerated or frozen. If refrigerated, bring to room temperature before baking. If frozen, bake without thawing for 2 hours or until hot.

Note: For optimal digestion, you may need to omit the eggs; plus omit the cheese or substitute soy cheese.

Serve with:
Tossed salad
Category A items of your choice
Category B items of your choice

Vegetarian Chili   **Category: B**   **Serves: 4**

This is one of my son Mickey's favorite dishes, and it's oh so easy to put together after a long work day.

1-15 oz. can red kidney beans, rinsed and drained
1/4 cup olive oil
1 large onion, chopped
1 red bell pepper, diced
4 cloves garlic, minced
1-14.5 oz. can diced tomatoes, undrained
4 cups vegetable broth
1-12 oz. package frozen veggie burger crumbles (I recommend Morning Star Farms)
1 heaping tablespoon chili powder
2 teaspoons ground cumin
1 teaspoon sugar
Salt and pepper to taste
Sour cream or Parmesan cheese for garnish (optional)
Cooked rice or pasta (optional)

In saucepot or Dutch oven, heat the oil and sauté the onion, bell pepper and garlic for 5 minutes. Stir in spices and cook for 1 minute, then add beans, broth, salt and pepper. Bring to a boil, reduce heat and simmer 10 minutes. Add tomatoes and veggie burger crumbles and return to a boil. Simmer uncovered for 20-30 minutes. Stir in sugar and let stand 5 minutes.

Serve alone or over rice or pasta, along with a dollop of sour cream or a sprinkling of Parmesan cheese on top.

Note: For optimal digestion, you may need to omit the sour cream and the cheese, or substitute soy cheese.

Serve with:
Italian bread
Category A items of your choice
Category B items of your choice

Golabki (Polish Stuffed Cabbage)   **Category: B**   **Serves: 4-6**

This is one of my mother Freida's recipes…modified a bit with veggie meats to make it properly combined.

1 very large head green cabbage or Savoy cabbage
1-1 lb. package brown rice
1 large onion, diced
1/2 cup butter or Earth Balance
2-12 oz. packages frozen veggie burger crumbles (I recommend Morning Star Farms)
1-10 oz. package vegetarian Italian sausage (I recommend Boca brand), thawed and diced finely
Salt and pepper to taste
5-10 oz. cans tomato soup (undiluted)
1 cup water
2 tablespoons cider vinegar

Preheat oven to 325°.

Rinse cabbage, remove a few of the outer leaves and cut out the bottom portion of the core. Fill a Dutch oven halfway with water. Place cabbage (core side down) in water, cover and bring to a boil. Steam cabbage, gradually peeling off leaves from the head with a fork or tongs as they soften and set aside. Add more water as necessary until all cabbage leaves are steamed and peeled away.

While cabbage steams, prepare rice as directed on box. Leave covered and set aside.

In a large skillet, sauté onion in butter over medium heat until soft. Stir in veggie burger crumbles and diced sausage and continue sautéing for another 8 minutes, adding more butter if necessary to keep meats and onion from sticking. Remove from heat, combine with prepared rice, season with salt and pepper to taste and mix well.

Place a cabbage leaf with sides curled upward and the core end nearest you on a plate or cutting board. Place 1/2 – 2/3 cup filling (depending on the size of the cabbage leaf) on the very bottom of the leaf, fold filling and bottom of leaf upward once, fold sides in tightly, then continue folding upward into a neat "pillow" shape. Place seam side down into a large roasting pan. Continue the process until all cabbage leaves and filling are gone.

In a large bowl, whisk together tomato soup concentrate, water and vinegar; pour over golabki in roasting pan.

Cover and bake at 325° for 2 1/2 hours. Ladle tomato soup sauce over golabki before serving.

Serve with:
Rye bread
Simple green salad
Category A items of your choice (without cheese)
Category B items of your choice

Greens and Beans   **Category: B**   **Serves: 4-6**

An Italian classic…

5 lbs. greens of your choice (escarole, endive, mustard greens, red or green Swiss chard, dandelion greens, collard greens or any combination thereof)
1 head garlic
1/2 cup olive oil
2-15 oz. cans Great Northern or cannellini beans, rinsed and drained
3 cups vegetable broth
3 cups Sherry Brescia's Outrageously Delicious Spaghetti Sauce (recipe on p. 67) or 1 jar store-bought spaghetti sauce
Grated Parmesan or Romano cheese for garnish (optional)
Cooked pasta of your choice (optional)

Rinse all greens and tear into bite-sized pieces.

Peel garlic and mince. Heat olive oil in large stockpot over medium heat, add garlic and sauté until fragrant but not browned.

Add greens, cover and cook over medium-low heat until greens begin to wilt. (If all greens don't fit in the pot at first, keep adding them in as the others wilt down.) Add broth and beans and bring to a boil. Reduce heat, cover and simmer until greens are tender.

Serve alone or over pasta, with a splash of spaghetti sauce on top. Sprinkle with grated cheese if desired.

Note: For optimal digestion, you may need to omit the cheese or substitute soy cheese if serving with pasta or bread.

Serve with:
Italian bread
Category A or Category B items of your choice

Delicious Panfried Fish   **Category: C**   **Serves: 5-6**

This fish will just melt in your mouth…

2 lbs. firm fish fillets of your choice (salmon and swordfish work very well)

For the marinade:
1 cup soy sauce
1/2 cup hot water
1/2 of a vegetable bullion cube
4 tablespoons olive oil
2 tablespoons brown sugar
4 teaspoons minced garlic
1 teaspoon ginger
Olive oil for frying

Poke a fork into various areas of each fish fillet to tenderize and make small holes for the marinade to seep into. Dissolve bullion cube half in hot water. Combine with other marinade ingredients and pour over fish. Marinate for at least 1 1/2 hours, turning at least twice and re-poking with a fork.

Cover the bottom of a large skillet with olive oil and heat over medium-high heat. Remove fish from marinade and place in skillet. Fry over high heat until done, turning once.

Fish should be cooked about 8-9 minutes per inch on medium-high heat. I recommend that you measure the thickness of your fish with a ruler and adjust the timing accordingly. Remember that fish continues to cook even after you remove it from the heat, so be careful not to overcook it. Always err on the side of underdone…you can always return the fish to the pan if it needs a bit more frying, but you can't un-cook dried out fish!

Serve with:
Spinach and Roasted Garlic Salad
Sautéed Broccoli Rabe
Category A items of your choice

Stuffed Peppers   **Category: B**   **Serves: 8 generously**

This is based on one of my mother's recipes, substituting veggie burger crumbles for the traditional ground beef. .

8 large bell peppers with flat bottoms (green, red, orange, yellow or any combination thereof)
6 cups Sherry Brescia's Outrageously Delicious Spaghetti Sauce (recipe on p. 67) or 2 jars store-bought spaghetti sauce, divided
3 cups brown or basmati rice
1-12 oz. package frozen veggie burger crumbles (I recommend Morning Star Farms)
1 medium onion, diced
1/4 cup olive oil, plus more for oiling baking pans
3 cloves garlic, minced
8 oz. fresh mushrooms, diced
3/4 cup Parmesan or Romano cheese, plus more for garnish (optional)

Preheat oven to 350°.

Carefully cut tops off of peppers and scoop out seeds, leaving pepper "cup" intact. Fill a large stockpot 2/3 full with water, bring to a boil and gently ease pepper cups into boiling water. Blanch for 3-4 minutes or just until slightly tender but not soft and pliable. Remove pepper cups from pot, drain well and set aside to cool.

Cook rice according to package directions; leave covered and set aside.

In a large skillet, sauté onion in olive oil over medium heat until soft, about 5 minutes. Add garlic, mushrooms and burger crumbles and continue to sauté another 5 minutes.

In a large bowl, combine rice, veggie burger mixture, 4 cups of spaghetti sauce and Parmesan or Romano cheese and mix well. Fill pepper cups to the top with mixture and place standing up in a lightly oiled baking or casserole dish. (Any extra filling may be eaten for lunch or it makes a terrific burrito filling!)

Bake covered at 350° for 45 minutes, then uncover and continue baking for another 15 minutes or until peppers are tender and filling is hot throughout. Serve topped with remaining 2 cups sauce if desired, and additional Parmesan or Romano cheese.

Note: For optimal digestion, you may need to omit the cheese or substitute soy cheese.

<u>Serve with:</u>
Tossed salad
Italian bread
Category A items of your choice
Category B items of your choice

Spanish Rice   **Category: B**   **Serves: 3-4**

This dish is delicious all on its own, or as a filling for burritos.

2 cups basmati rice
1/4 cup olive oil
1 large onion, diced
1 green bell pepper, diced
4 cloves garlic, minced
3/4 cup tomato puree
1 1/2 teaspoons salt
1 heaping tablespoon ground cumin
2 3/4 cups vegetable broth
3/4 cup frozen petite or regular peas

Heat oil in large skillet over medium-high heat. Add rice and sauté until golden brown (about 8-10 minutes). Add onion and bell pepper and sauté another 5 minutes. Add garlic and sauté another 2 minutes.

Stir in tomato puree, vegetable broth, salt and cumin and raise heat to high. Bring to a full boil, reduce heat to low, cover and simmer for 20 minutes. Remove from heat, stir in peas and cover. Let sit for 5 minutes and serve.

Serve with:
Fresh Salsa
Sliced tomato salad
Sherry's Garlic Green Beans
Category A items of your choice
Category B items of your choice

Shrimp Scampi   **Category: C**   **Serves: 4-6**

Easy and elegant—a great combination!

2 lbs. large or jumbo uncooked shrimp, shelled and deveined
1/2 cup butter or Earth Balance
1 teaspoon salt
6 cloves garlic, crushed
1/4 cup chopped fresh parsley
2 tablespoons fresh lemon juice

Preheat oven to 400°.

Melt butter in oven in a 13"x 9"x 2" pan. Remove from oven and stir in salt, garlic and half of the parsley.

Add shrimp and stir to coat. Bake uncovered for 5 minutes. Remove from oven, turn shrimp over, sprinkle with lemon juice and remaining parsley.

Bake for another 3-4 minutes or until shrimp are done. (Be careful not to overcook.)

Remove shrimp from pan, place on a serving platter or bowl, pour garlic-butter sauce from pan over shrimp and serve.

Serve with:
Not the Spinach You Grew Up With
Tossed Salad
Category A items of your choice

Salmon With Brown Sugar Glaze **Category: C** **Serves: 4-6**

The spicy sweet glaze is the perfect compliment to the moist, tender fish.

3/4 cup dry white wine
1/4 cup butter or Earth Balance
2 teaspoons Old Bay Seasoning (or other seafood seasoning blend)
2 lbs. salmon fillets
1/3 cup spicy brown mustard
1/4 cup brown sugar

Preheat oven to 375°.

Combine wine, butter and Old Bay Seasoning in a small saucepan; bring to a boil and simmer 3 minutes. Remove from heat.

Place fish in a baking dish, pour wine-butter sauce over. Bake for 5 minutes.

Meanwhile, combine mustard and sugar in a small bowl.

Remove fish from oven and raise heat to broil setting. Spread mustard-sugar mixture over fish, place under broiler and broil until topping is bubbly; about 3 minutes. Serve at once.

Note: It's important not to overcook fish. The instructions above are for fish fillets that are about 1" thick. Generally, fish should be cooked about 8-9 minutes per inch. You may need to adjust the initial baking time accordingly if your fish fillets are thicker or thinner than 1". Remember—you can always return the fish to the oven or broiler if it's not quite done to your liking, but you can't un-cook overdone fish!

Serve with:
Green Beans Almondine
Tossed salad
Category A items of your choice

Greek Baked Vegetables   **Category: B**   **Serves: 6-8 generously**

This is an authentic Greek dish. Try to use the best feta you can find.

2 lbs. zucchini
2 lbs. potatoes (any kind)
2 1/2 lbs. eggplant
1 large Vidalia onion, diced
2 red or green bell peppers, seeded and cut into slices
1-28 oz. can diced tomatoes
1-15 oz. can diced tomatoes
1 cup chopped fresh parsley
1 1/4 cups olive oil, plus additional for drizzling
1 1/2 cups crumbled feta cheese
Salt and pepper to taste

Preheat oven to 350°.

Wash zucchini and eggplant; cut into bite-sized chunks.   Scrub potatoes, cut in half lengthwise, then cut each half into 1/4" slices.

Combine all ingredients in a very large bowl; toss and mix well. Turn into a large roasting pan and bake for 1 1/2 hours or until all vegetables are tender. Check and stir vegetables every 1/2 hour while baking, drizzling additional olive oil if they appear dry.

Note: For optimal digestion, you may need to omit the cheese, or substitute soy cheese, or substitute additional zucchini, eggplant and peppers to replace the potatoes.

Serve with:
Tossed salad
Category A items of your choice
Category B items of your choice

Liana's Homemade Pizza   **Category: B**   **Serves: 3-4**

This recipe is the creation of my very dear friend Liana. We have a lot in common—a love for martial arts, running and most of all, great food!

Pizza Crust

Note: This recipe is designed to be cooked on a well-seasoned pizza stone (14"). If you don't have a pizza stone you will need to oil your pan and sprinkle with cornmeal to prevent the pizza from sticking. If your pan is thin, watch the pizza closely so that the crust does not burn (consider using a lower oven temperature and longer cooking time).

1 package active dry yeast
1 cup warm water (approx. 110°)
1/8 cup olive oil, plus additional for rubbing onto dough
1/4 cup chopped fresh basil leaves (or 1/8 cup dried basil)
2 1/2 cups flour
1/2 to 3/4 teaspoon salt (to taste)

Dissolve yeast in water. Add oil and basil to yeast water. Combine flour and salt in a separate bowl then add to yeast water. Mix until thoroughly combined. (It works well to add the first 2 1/4 cups flour/salt mixture and mix with a large serving fork; then spread the remaining 1/4 cup flour onto your work surface and mix by hand until all the flour is absorbed.)

Form dough into a ball. Coat your hands with 1/4 to 1/2 teaspoon oil and then rub into the dough ball. Put in a covered bowl and let rise for about 20 minutes.

Preheat pizza stone and oven to 425°. Stretch or roll the dough out to form the crust and place on stone. Use a fork to prick the dough thoroughly.

Pre-cook the dough for 10 minutes (to prevent the toppings from getting burned). Add desired toppings and cook for another 10-12 minutes or until done.

Tomato and Goat Cheese Pizza

Pizza sauce (optional)
3/4 cup whole fresh basil leaves, or enough to cover pizza dough
3 large very ripe tomatoes, sliced
1/4 cup Parmesan cheese
4 oz. crumbled goat cheese
1 cup pizza/mozzarella cheese (optional)

(For an extra moist pizza coat the precooked pizza crust with a small amount of pizza sauce.) Top precooked crust with basil leaves and place tomatoes on top to keep the basil from drying out. Sprinkle with parmesan cheese, goat cheese, and pizza cheese, if using.

Bake for 10-12 minutes until dough is cooked through and cheeses are melted.

Note: For optimal digestion, you may need to substitute soy cheese or omit cheese altogether and serve it as tomato pie.

Serve with:
Tossed salad
Category A items of your choice

Potato Pancakes   **Category: B**   **Serves: 3-4**

My mother would make these for dinner on Friday evenings during the Catholic Lenten season. There were never any leftovers!

1 lb. potatoes
1/2 cup chopped onion
1 large egg, beaten
1/2 teaspoon salt
3/4 cup olive oil (or more if needed)
Butter and/or sour cream for garnish (optional)

Preheat oven to 250°. Peel potatoes and grate, transferring to a large bowl of cold water as they are grated. Once the last batch of potatoes is added to the water, soak for 1-2 minutes, then drain thoroughly in a colander. Spread the grated potatoes onto an old, large kitchen towel, roll up jelly-roll style and twist towel to wring out as much liquid as possible. Place potatoes in a large mixing bowl; stir in onion, egg and salt and mix well to combine.

Heat approximately 1/4 cup olive oil in a large skillet over medium-high heat. Drop batter by 1/4 cupfuls per pancake into skillet, flattening slightly with a fork. Reduce heat to medium and cook until both sides are brown and crispy, about 5 minutes per side. Remove from skillet, drain on paper towels and season with salt. Keep warm in a shallow baking dish in the oven. Repeat process with the remainder of the batter.

Top with butter and/or sour cream.

Note: For optimal digestion, you may need to use an egg replacer—2 tablespoons cornstarch beaten in 2 tablespoons of water—instead of the egg; and omit the sour cream garnish.

Serve with:
Sherry's Garlic Green Beans
Simple green salad with olive oil and vinegar
Category A items of your choice

Shrimp With Basil-Garlic Sauce   **Category: C**   **Serves: 3-4**

A little different twist on the classic shrimp scampi.

1 1/2 lbs. extra large or jumbo shrimp, shelled and deveined
5 tablespoons olive oil
5 cloves garlic, minced
1/3 cup dry white wine
1 scant tablespoon fresh lemon juice
3 tablespoons sundried tomatoes packed in oil, diced
3/4 cup butter or Earth Balance
1/2 cup chopped fresh basil leaves
Salt and pepper to taste

Preheat oven to 350°.

Heat olive oil in a large skillet over medium-high heat. Sauté shrimp 1 minute per side, remove and place in baking dish. Bake shrimp until just cooked through, about 6-7 minutes.

While shrimp is baking, add garlic to skillet and sauté briefly until fragrant but not browned. Stir in wine, lemon juice and tomatoes. Bring to a boil, reduce heat and simmer until reduced by two-thirds. Stir in basil and butter and add salt and pepper to taste.

Remove shrimp from oven, pour sauce over and serve.

Serve with:
Green Beans Almondine
Tossed salad
Category A items of your choice

Salmon With Horseradish Sauce   **Category: C**   **Serves: 6**

This is also delicious made with swordfish or sea bass.

Horseradish Sauce:
3/4 cup sour cream
1/4 cup mayonnaise
3 tablespoons prepared horseradish
3 tablespoons chopped fresh basil leaves
1 tablespoon fresh lemon juice
Salt and pepper to taste

Fish:
6-1" thick salmon fillets
4 tablespoons olive oil
1 tablespoon prepared horseradish
1 tablespoon tamari (soy sauce)
2 cloves garlic, minced
1/4 teaspoon pepper

Preheat oven to broil setting. Mix all sauce ingredients together in a small bowl. Cover and chill.

Combine olive oil, horseradish, tamari, garlic and pepper. Place fish on broiler pan, brush with olive oil mixture and broil 4 minutes. Turn fish, brush with remaining oil mixture and broil another 3 minutes or until done, being careful not to overcook.

Place fish on a platter and serve with horseradish sauce.

Serve with:
Summer Squash Sauté
Tossed salad
Category A items of your choice

Red Lentil Stew   **Category: B**   **Serves: 4**

An earthy stew filled with tasty, fragrant spices.

3 tablespoons olive oil
1 medium onion, chopped
1 teaspoon saffron threads, crushed
1 tablespoon hot water
1 teaspoon curry powder
2 teaspoons ground cumin
1 teaspoon rosemary, crushed
1 teaspoon fennel seeds
6 cups vegetable broth
1-15 oz. can Great Northern or cannellini beans, rinsed and drained
1/2 cup red lentils
1/2 cup basmati rice
1 tomato, diced
1/3 cup chopped fresh cilantro
1 tablespoon tomato paste
Salt and pepper to taste

Mix the saffron and hot water together in a small bowl and set aside.

Heat the oil in a Dutch oven over medium heat. Add onion and sauté 5 minutes.

Add the curry powder, cumin, rosemary and fennel seeds to the Dutch oven and stir. Add the saffron mixture, vegetable broth, beans, lentils and rice and stir. Bring to a boil over high heat, then reduce heat, cover and simmer 30 minutes or until lentils are tender.

Stir in tomato, cilantro and tomato paste. Add salt and pepper to taste.

<u>Serve with:</u>
Simple green salad
Pita bread
Category A items of your choice
Category B items of your choice

Spaghetti Puttanesca　　　　　　　**Category: B**　　　　　　　**Serves: 3-4**

This is a flavor-packed dish. If you're not an anchovy fan, try using a dab of anchovy paste instead.

1/2 lb. spaghetti
4 tablespoons olive oil, plus more for drizzling
3 cloves garlic, minced
1 small fresh red chili, diced or 1 small dried red chili, crumbled
1-2 oz. can anchovy fillets, chopped
1-14 oz. can diced tomatoes
3/4 cup pitted kalamata or black olives
2 tablespoons capers, rinsed
1 tablespoon tomato paste
2 tablespoons chopped fresh parsley
Grated Parmesan or Romano cheese for garnish

Heat olive oil in a Dutch oven over medium heat. Add garlic and chili and cook until garlic is fragrant but not browned. Add anchovies, mashing them into garlic with a fork. Add tomatoes, olives, capers and tomato paste. Stir and cook over medium heat.

Meanwhile, bring a large pan of water to a boil and cook spaghetti according to package directions. Drain. Add spaghetti to sauce in Dutch oven, toss to combine and cook for another 1-2 minutes. Sprinkle with parsley and serve.

Add Parmesan or Romano cheese or drizzle with additional olive oil as a garnish if desired.

Note: For optimal digestion, you may need to omit the cheese or substitute soy cheese; and omit the anchovies.

Serve with:
Italian Bread
Tossed salad
Category A items of your choice
Category B items of your choice

Pan Bagnat   **Category: B**   **Serves: 3 generously**

This is perfect to take to a picnic or for "tailgating" before a ball game.

1 loaf French bread
1/4 cup olive oil
2 cloves garlic, pressed
2/3 cup basil pesto (for homemade, see recipe on p. 34)
4 oz. sliced sharp provolone cheese
1 large tomato, sliced thin
1 large cucumber, sliced thin
2/3 cup black olives, sliced
1/2 green bell pepper, sliced thin
1/2 red bell pepper, sliced thin
1-14 oz. can artichoke hearts, drained and sliced
1/2 small red onion, thinly sliced

Preheat oven to 350°.

Slice bread in half lengthwise, almost all the way through, but not quite. Lay bread halves on a large sheet of aluminum foil covering your work area, cut side up. Combine olive oil and garlic and drizzle on bread halves. Spread pesto evenly over both halves.

Layer ingredients on one half of the bread. Carefully close the sandwich up, tucking ingredients back in if they fall out. (You may need an extra pair of hands to help if someone else is around!) Wrap sandwich tightly in 2 layers of foil. Bake for 20-30 minutes until bread is slightly toasty and cheese is melted. Cut and serve when desired.

Note: For optimal digestion, you may need to omit the cheese or substitute soy cheese.

Serve with:
Pickles
Category A or Category B items of your choice

Vegetarian Chili with Bulgur Wheat   **Category: B**   **Serves: 4-6**

This is packed with great flavor and lots of textures.

1/2 cup bulgur wheat
1 1/2 cups water
4 tablespoons olive oil
1 large Vidalia onion, diced
4 garlic cloves, minced
2-3 teaspoons ground cumin (more for spicier chili)
1 tablespoon chili powder
1/2 teaspoon cayenne pepper
2 green or red bell peppers (or one of each), chopped
1-28 oz. can diced tomatoes (undrained)
2 cups fresh or frozen corn
1-15 oz. can black beans, rinsed and drained
1-15 oz. can kidney beans, rinsed and drained
Salt and pepper to taste
Grated Parmesan or Romano cheese or sour cream for garnish (optional)

Place the bulgur and water in a small saucepan. Bring to a boil over high heat. Reduce heat, cover and simmer slowly until tender but slightly chewy. Leave covered and set aside.

Heat olive oil in a Dutch oven or soup pot over medium heat. Sauté the onions, garlic, cumin, chili powder, and cayenne until onions begin to soften, about 5 minutes.

Stir in the peppers and sauté for 2–3 minutes more. Add tomatoes, corn and beans, bring to a boil, then reduce heat and simmer uncovered for 10 minutes.

Add bulgur wheat, season with salt and pepper to taste, stir well to combine and heat for 2-3 more minutes. Top with grated Parmesan or Romano cheese or a dollop of sour cream as a garnish, if desired.

Note: For optimal digestion, you may need to omit the cheese and sour cream, or substitute soy cheese.

Serve with:
French bread
Category A items of your choice
Category B items of your choice

Seafood Stew   **Category: C**   **Serves: 6**

My husband Mike and I had this dish in a restaurant when we were out to dinner celebrating our anniversary. It was so delicious that I tried my best to duplicate it at home. Mike swears it tastes the same!

1 large Vidalia onion, chopped
1/4 cup olive oil
3 stalks celery, chopped
1 green bell pepper, chopped
1 red bell pepper, chopped
5 garlic cloves, pressed
Pinch of crushed red pepper flakes
2 teaspoons dried oregano
1 teaspoon dried marjoram
3 tablespoons chopped fresh basil leaves (or 1 tablespoon dried)
2 cups bottled clam juice
1-28 oz. can crushed tomatoes
2/3 cup dry red wine
1 lb. firm white fish fillets (such as swordfish or orange roughy), cut into 1" cubes
1 pound scallops, rinsed and halved if very large
1 pound extra large shrimp, shelled and deveined
1 tablespoon fresh lemon juice
Salt and pepper to taste
Grated Parmesan or Romano cheese for garnish

Heat olive oil in a Dutch oven or soup pot over medium heat. Add onions and sauté 5 minutes. Add celery and peppers and sauté for 2 more minutes.

Stir in garlic, crushed red pepper flakes, oregano, marjoram and basil. Lower the heat, cover and cook for 2 minutes. Add the clam juice, tomatoes, and wine. Cover and simmer for 15 minutes.

Add the fish, scallops and shrimp, and cook until the seafood is just done—about 4-5 minutes. Stir in lemon juice and season with salt and pepper to taste.

Top with grated Parmesan or Romano cheese if desired.

Serve with:
Tossed Salad or *Caesar Salad*
Broccoli With Garlic and Cheese
Category A items of your choice

Tangy Vegetable Stew **Category: B** **Serves: 4**

This dish has a lot of German influence and a nicely robust flavor.

1 large onion, chopped
3 tablespoons olive oil
3 carrots, sliced
2 stalks celery, chopped
2 large potatoes, cubed
2 parsnips, diced
2 cups fresh or frozen green beans, cut into 1" pieces
1 tablespoon chopped fresh dill
1 teaspoon dried marjoram
1 1/2 cups water
1 cup dark beer
1 red bell pepper, chopped
8 oz. white mushrooms, sliced
1 tablespoon molasses
1 teaspoon spicy brown mustard
Salt and pepper to taste

Heat oil in a Dutch oven or soup pot over medium heat. Add onion and sauté onion 5 minutes. Add carrots and celery and sauté 3 minutes. Add potatoes, parsnips and beans and sauté another 2 minutes.

Stir in dill, marjoram, water and beer and bring to a boil. Reduce heat, cover and simmer for 10 minutes. Add pepper and mushrooms and continue simmering for 5 minutes. Add the mustard and molasses and continue to simmer for about 10 minutes, or until all vegetables are tender. Add salt and pepper to taste.

Serve with:
Dark bread (such as whole grain or pumpernickel)
Category A items of your choice
Category B items of your choice

Feta and Tomato Shrimp Scampi   **Category: C**   **Serves: 4-6**

This might quickly become your standard choice for Christmas dinner instead of turkey or ham! Recipe may be doubled or tripled for a larger crowd.

2 lbs. extra large shrimp, shelled and deveined
8 cloves garlic, pressed
8 tablespoons olive oil
4 cups tomatoes, diced
2 1/2 cups feta cheese, crumbled
1 tablespoon fresh lemon juice
1/4 cup chopped fresh dill
Salt and pepper to taste

In a very large skillet, heat oil over medium heat. Sauté garlic until fragrant but not browned. Add shrimp and cook for 1-2 minutes.

Add the tomatoes, feta, lemon juice, and dill. Continue to cook and stir, turning shrimp over so they cook on both sides, for 5 minutes or until shrimp are done. Be careful not to overcook—test shrimp for doneness if in doubt.

Add salt and pepper to taste and serve.

Serve with:
Tossed salad
Category A items of your choice

Corn Burritos   **Category: B**   **Serves: 4**

Kids love these...and so do adults!

Filling:
2 tablespoons olive oil
1 medium onion, chopped
2 cloves garlic, minced
1 large red or green bell pepper, chopped
1 fresh chile, seeded and diced
3 cups fresh or frozen corn
2 teaspoons ground cumin
1 teaspoon ground coriander
1 tablespoon chopped fresh cilantro (or 1 teaspoon dried)
Salt and ground black pepper to taste

Other burrito ingredients:
Whole wheat flour tortillas
Grated cheddar cheese (optional)
Sour cream (optional)
Sliced black olives
Diced tomatoes
Shredded lettuce

Heat the oil in a large skillet over medium heat. Add onion and garlic and sauté for 5 minutes. Stir in bell pepper and sauté for 3 more minutes. Add the chile, corn, cumin, coriander, and cilantro; cover and cook for 5 minutes, stirring occasionally. Add salt and pepper to taste. Assemble burritos using other ingredients as desired.

Note: For optimal digestion, you may need to omit the cheese and sour cream, or substitute soy cheese.

Serve with:
Fresh Salsa

Cod with Dill Sauce   **Category: C**   **Serves: 4**

The dill sauce is the perfect match for the mild-flavored fish.

2 leeks, white and tender green parts, thinly sliced and soaked in water to remove sand
6 tablespoons olive oil, divided
2 garlic cloves, minced
1/2 teaspoon dried savory
1 1/2 cups vegetable broth
1/2 cup dry white wine
1 tablespoon butter or Earth Balance
4-8 oz. cod fillets
Salt and freshly ground black pepper
Unbleached flour for dredging
2 tablespoons minced fresh dill, plus more for garnish

In a large skillet over medium heat, sauté the leeks in 2 tablespoons of the oil until soft, about 3-4 minutes. Add the garlic, savory, broth and wine. Raise the heat to high and cook until the liquid has been reduced by half, about 12-15 minutes. Put the mixture in a food processor or blender, add the butter and puree. Pour into a small bowl, set aside and cover to keep warm.

Sprinkle the cod with salt and pepper, and lightly dredge in flour. Heat the remaining 4 tablespoons olive oil over high heat in the same skillet. Add the cod fillets and sauté, turning once, until golden, about 2-3 minutes per side. Be careful not to overcook.

Arrange fish on a serving platter. Stir the dill into the sauce and season to taste with salt and pepper. Pour the sauce over the fish. Garnish with additional dill, if desired.

Note: For optimal digestion, you may need to omit the dredging flour.

Serve with:
Asparagus With Pine Nuts and Balsamic Vinegar
Category A items of your choice

Salmon with Raspberry Sauce Category: C Serves: 4

This is truly a restaurant-style dish, yet surprisingly easy to make.

2 tablespoons butter or Earth Balance, divided
2 medium shallots, minced
1/2 cup raspberry vinegar
1/2 pint fresh raspberries
1 teaspoon honey
Salt and pepper to taste
4-6 oz. salmon fillets
3 tablespoons olive oil

Melt 1 tablespoon of the butter in a small sauce pan over low heat. Add the shallots and cook for 3-4 minutes or until translucent. Add the vinegar, raise the heat to medium- high, and boil for 1 minute.

Lower the heat to medium, add the berries, and cook until thick, about 15 minutes. Strain over a heatproof bowl, pressing the solids with the back of a spoon or the bottom of a flat-bottomed glass to strain out all of the liquid. Return liquid to the sauce pan. Simmer for about 5 minutes to thicken, then whisk in the remaining tablespoon of butter and the honey over low heat. Season to taste with salt and pepper. Set aside and keep warm.

Generously season the salmon with salt and pepper. Heat the olive oil in a large skillet over medium-high heat. Add the salmon and cook until golden, about 4 minutes per side. Be careful not to overcook.

Arrange the salmon on a serving platter and serve with the warm raspberry sauce drizzled over.

Serve with:
Tossed salad or *Spinach and Roasted Garlic Salad*
Category A items of your choice

Sea Bass with Feta   **Category: C**   **Serves: 4**

This recipe seems almost too simple to be anything special...but it's exquisite!

1/4 cup Italian bread crumbs
4 oz. feta cheese, crumbled
1 tablespoon olive oil
1 tablespoon minced fresh dill
1 tablespoon minced fresh chives
Salt and freshly ground pepper to taste
4-7 oz. sea bass fillets (or any firm whitefish, such as orange roughy)

Preheat oven to 375°.

Combine the bread crumbs, cheese, oil, dill, and chives in a small bowl; mix well.

Generously salt and pepper the bass and place on a lightly greased baking sheet or casserole dish. Press the breadcrumb mixture on top of each fillet. Bake uncovered, until the fish is firm and cooked through, about 10-15 minutes.

Note: For optimal digestion, you may need to omit the breadcrumbs.

Serve with:
Tossed salad
Yellow Squash With Basil
Category A items of your choice

Spicy Red Beans and Rice   **Category: B**   **Serves: 4**

This is great as an entrée, or also doubles as a burrito filling.

2 tablespoons olive oil
1 medium onion, chopped
3 garlic cloves, minced
1 green or red bell pepper, diced
1 stalk celery, chopped
1 1/2 teaspoons thyme leaves
1/2 teaspoon cayenne pepper
3 cups vegetable broth
1 1/2 cups brown or basmati rice
1/2 teaspoon seasoned salt
1-16 oz. can kidney beans, rinsed and drained
Grated cheddar cheese or sour cream for garnish (optional)

Heat oil in a Dutch oven or large saucepan over medium-high heat. Add onion, garlic, pepper, celery, thyme and cayenne and sauté until tender, about 10 minutes.

Stir in broth, rice and seasoned salt. Bring to a boil, cover, reduce heat and simmer for 20 minutes or until rice is tender (brown rice may take longer).

Add beans, stir and heat for a moment. Top with grated cheddar cheese or a dollop of sour cream for garnish if desired.

Note: For optimal digestion, you may need to omit the cheese and sour cream, or substitute soy cheese.

Serve with:
Tossed salad
Category A items of your choice
Category B items of your choice

Black Bean Chili   **Category: B**   **Serves: 4**

This is perfect on a chilly winter day.

3 tablespoons olive oil
1 large onion, diced
5 cloves garlic, minced
4 teaspoons ground cumin
2 teaspoons chili powder
4 teaspoons dried oregano
1/2 teaspoon cayenne pepper
3-16 oz. cans black beans, rinsed and drained
1-15 oz. can diced tomatoes, undrained
Salt and pepper to taste
Sour cream for garnish (optional)

Heat oil in a Dutch oven or large saucepan over medium heat. Add onions and sauté 5 minutes. Add garlic and sauté an additional 2 minutes. Stir in cumin, chili powder, oregano and cayenne.

Add beans and tomatoes and salt and pepper to taste. Bring to a boil, reduce heat to low and simmer, uncovered, for 15-20 minutes.

Serve alone or over rice or pasta, with a dollop of sour cream as a garnish if desired.

Note: For optimal digestion, you may need to omit the sour cream.

Serve with:
Tossed salad
Italian bread
Category A items of your choice
Category B items of your choice

Eggplant Lasagna   **Category: C**   **Serves: 6**

This is a little different twist on traditional lasagna. Roasted eggplant slices take the place of lasagna noodles, there's a cheesy spinach filling in the middle, with a custard-y white sauce topping.

2 large eggplants
1 large Vidalia onion, diced
3 cloves garlic, pressed
1/2 cup olive oil, divided
1 lb. fresh spinach
1 large baking potato
1-16 oz. carton ricotta cheese (part skim works well)
1 egg, lightly beaten
3 tablespoons butter or Earth Balance
3 tablespoons unbleached flour
1 cup milk
2 egg yolks
Salt and pepper to taste
2 cups Sherry Brescia's Outrageously Delicious Spaghetti Sauce (see recipe on p. 67) or 1 jar store-bought spaghetti sauce, divided
1 cup grated Parmesan or Romano cheese, divided

Preheat oven to 375°.

Wash and slice eggplant into 1/2" rounds. Brush with olive oil, place on baking sheet and roast for 12-15 minutes. Remove from oven and set aside. Lower oven to 350°.

Heat remaining olive oil in a Dutch oven over medium heat. Sauté onion until tender, about 5 minutes. Add garlic and sauté 2 minutes more. Remove from heat and set aside.

Lightly steam spinach until just wilted. Drain, squeeze dry and chop.

Prick potato with a fork, microwave on high for 6-7 minutes or until tender. Cool slightly, dice then mash with a fork. (Or, you can dice raw potato and cook in a saucepan of water until tender; drain and mash.)

In a large bowl, combine onion and garlic (with olive oil from sauté pan), spinach, potato, egg and ricotta cheese. Mix well.

Beat egg yolks in a small bowl and set aside.

Melt butter in a small saucepan over medium heat. Stir in flour until well-combined, then gradually add milk, stirring with a wire whisk to keep smooth. Add salt and pepper to taste, and cook until thickened.

Stir a few tablespoons of hot milk mixture into egg yolks, then pour yolk mixture into milk mixture. Stir well and set aside.

Place 1 cup of spaghetti sauce on bottom of a 9"x 13" baking pan or large shallow casserole dish. Place half of eggplant slices on top of sauce, cover with half of cheese-spinach mixture and sprinkle with 1/4 cup Parmesan or Romano cheese.

Cover with remaining 1 cup sauce, then create a second layer with remaining eggplant, spinach-cheese mixture and 1/4 cup Parmesan or Romano.

Pour milk-egg sauce over all, sprinkle with remaining 1/2 cup Parmesan or Romano.

Bake, uncovered for 35-45 minutes.

Note: For optimal digestion, you may need to omit the potato.

Serve with:
Tossed salad
Category A items of your choice

Bubble & Squeak (Fried Potatoes and Cabbage)   **Serves: 3-4**
Category: B

If you have a cast iron skillet, be sure to use it for this recipe! If not, any heavy-duty skillet will do.

1 lb. russet baking potatoes
1/2 cup butter or Earth Balance
1 large onion, diced
1 lb. green or Savoy cabbage, cored and thinly sliced
3/4 teaspoon salt
1/2 teaspoon freshly ground black pepper

Peel potatoes and cut into 1" chunks.

Place potatoes in Dutch oven, cover with cold water and bring to a boil. Boil, uncovered, until tender (about 15 minutes). Drain.

Heat butter in a skillet over medium-high heat. Sauté onion until slightly browned and carmelized, about 10 minutes. Add cabbage with salt and pepper and sauté until tender, about 5-10 more minutes. (You may need to add a bit more butter or Earth Balance if vegetables start to stick or get too brown.)

Add potatoes, mashing and stirring into cabbage (leave some of the potatoes lumpy). Press with a large spoon or spatula to form a cake.

Cook without turning until the underside is golden and crusty, about 10 minutes. Serve at once with additional butter, salt and pepper.

Serve with:
Sherry's Peas and Carrots
Asparagus With Pine Nuts and Balsamic Vinegar
Tossed salad
Crusty bread

Vegetable Sides

Italian Cauliflower   **Category: A/C**   **Serves: 4-6**

Who said cauliflower is a boring vegetable? Not when you make it this way!

1 large head (or 2 small heads) cauliflower, broken into florets
3 cloves garlic, minced
1/2 cup olive oil, plus more for drizzling
1/2 cup grated Parmesan or Romano cheese
1/2 tsp. salt or garlic salt
1/4 tsp. freshly ground black pepper

Preheat oven to 350°.

Rinse and steam cauliflower until slightly tender. Drain, return to pot and set aside. Sauté garlic in olive oil until fragrant but not browned.

Stir garlic and oil into drained cauliflower; add cheese, sprinkle with salt and pepper and mix well. Turn cauliflower into a casserole or baking dish. Drizzle with a little extra olive oil.

Bake uncovered for 20-30 minutes, until slightly browned on top.

This is equally delicious with 2 bunches of broccoli, or a mixture of broccoli and cauliflower.

Serve with:
Category A items of your choice, and
Category B items of your choice (for optimal digestion, you may need to omit the cheese or substitute soy cheese) **OR**
Category C items of your choice (Steak, chicken, sausage and fish all go well)

Freida's Kapusta   **Category: A**   **Serves: 6-8**

This is my dear mother's recipe.

1 large head green cabbage
2 cups water
1-27 oz. can sauerkraut
1 medium white onion, diced
1/2 cup butter
Salt and pepper to taste

Shred cabbage and place in a large Dutch oven or saucepot. Add water, cover, bring to a boil and steam cabbage on medium-low heat for 15 minutes.

While cabbage cooks, sauté onion in butter in a medium frying pan until tender. Set aside.

Drain off and reserve about half of the water from the cabbage. Return cabbage and remaining water in Dutch oven to stove. Add sauerkraut, sautéed onion and butter, and salt and pepper to taste. Bring to a boil, reduce heat and simmer covered, stirring occasionally, for another 30-45 minutes or until desired tenderness (be sure not to overcook). Add reserved cabbage water 1/2 cup at a time as needed if cabbage appears too dry. Taste and correct the seasoning.

Serve with:
Category A items of your choice, and
Category B items of your choice **OR**
Category C items of your choice (Kielbasa or corned beef go well)

Sherry's Garlic Green Beans   **Category: A**   **Serves: 8-10**

Without fail, I am asked to make these for every family holiday dinner and there are NEVER any leftovers!

2 1/2 lbs. fresh green beans, trimmed, washed and broken into 2" pieces
8 cloves garlic, minced
1/2 cup olive oil, plus more for drizzling
Garlic salt and pepper to taste

Steam green beans in a large saucepot or Dutch over just until tender; drain and return to pan.

Sauté garlic in olive oil until fragrant but not browned. Remove from heat; pour garlic and oil from pan over green beans and stir well to combine. Season with garlic salt and pepper to taste, and drizzle with additional olive oil if needed.

<u>Serve with:</u>
Category A items of your choice, and
Category B items of your choice **OR**
Category C items of your choice (Steak or fish go well)

Sherry's Peas and Carrots   **Category: B**   **Serves: 3-4**

These are a nice twist to this classic combination, and make a terrific addition to a holiday dinner.

1 lb. baby carrots
1 lb. sugar snap pea pods
1/3 cup butter or Earth Balance
2 tablespoons maple syrup
1/4 cup fresh basil, chopped
Salt and pepper to taste.

Lightly steam carrots and pea pods until crisp-tender. Drain.

Toss with butter, maple syrup and basil. Season with salt and pepper to taste.

Serve with:
Bubble and Squeak
Category A items of your choice
Category B items of your choice

Broccoli with Garlic and Cheese   **Category: A/C**   **Serves: 5-6**

When my daughter was small, she would ask me to make "Mommy's trees" for dinner.

2 bunches broccoli, tops broken into florets and stalks peeled and diced
8 cloves garlic, minced
1/2 cup olive oil, plus more for drizzling
1/2 teaspoon salt or garlic salt
2/3 cup Parmesan or Romano cheese, plus more for sprinkling

Lightly steam broccoli until just tender; drain.

Sauté garlic in oil until fragrant but not browned.

Toss all ingredients together. Drizzle with additional olive oil or sprinkle with additional cheese if desired.

Serve with:
Category A items of your choice, and
Category B items of your choice (for optimal digestion, you may need to omit the cheese or substitute soy cheese) **OR**
Category C items of your choice (Steak, chicken or fish all go well)

Yummy Fried Potatoes   **Category: B**   **Serves: 4-6**

These are comfort food at its best.

6 large red or golden butter potatoes, unpeeled
1 large Vidalia onion, diced
1 red bell pepper, sliced
1 green bell pepper, sliced
8 oz. fresh mushrooms, sliced
1/2 cup butter or Earth Balance, divided
1/2 cup olive oil
1 tablespoon dried oregano
1 tablespoon chili powder
1 1/2 teaspoons salt or seasoned salt
1 teaspoon pepper (preferably freshly ground)

If you have a large cast iron skillet, be sure to use it for this recipe! However, any large skillet will work just fine.

Scrub potatoes and cut into small chunks. Heat olive oil and 1/4 cup butter over medium heat in a very large skillet; add potatoes. Cook, flipping potatoes with a spatula occasionally for 15 minutes. Add onion and continue cooking for another 5 minutes. Add peppers and cook for another 8 minutes, continuing to flip potatoes, onions and peppers occasionally. (Add additional 1/4 cup butter if necessary to prevent sticking.)

Add mushrooms, oregano, chili powder, salt and pepper. Continue cooking as above until all vegetables are tender, potatoes are browned and crisp and onions are caramelized. Add additional salt and pepper to taste.

Serve with:
Tossed salad
Category A items of your choice
Category B items of your choice

Roasted Garlic Mashed Potatoes   **Category: B**   **Serves: 6-8**

Those who prepare traditional mashed potatoes with an electric mixer might find these a bit "odd"...but the slightly lumpy texture along with the bits of roasted garlic is part of the experience of this delicious dish. Resist the temptation to use your mixer, and instead dig out the old-fashioned potato masher!

1 head garlic, peeled
2 tablespoons olive oil
10 large red or golden butter potatoes, unpeeled
1/2 cup butter or Earth Balance
1/2 cup milk, light cream, rice milk or soy milk
1 teaspoon salt or garlic salt
1/2 teaspoon pepper (preferably freshly ground)

Preheat oven to 375°. Place garlic cloves in a small baking dish or foil packet, drizzle with olive oil and sprinkle with salt. Roast for 30-40 minutes until golden brown and soft when pierced with a sharp knife. Remove from oven, pour garlic and oil into a small bowl and mash garlic in oil with a fork. Set aside.

Scrub potatoes, cut into cubes and cook in boiling water in Dutch oven or saucepot until tender (about 20-30 minutes, depending on size of the cubes). Drain and return to pan.

Add butter to potatoes and mash with a potato masher until slightly smooth, but letting some lumps and chunks remain. Add milk or cream, salt and pepper and mash a little more. Stir in garlic and oil and serve. Note: If a thinner consistency is preferred, stir in additional milk or cream by tablespoons until desired consistency is reached.

Note: For optimal digestion, you may need to use rice milk or soy milk instead of cow's milk or cream.

Serve with:
Kapusta
Tossed salad
Category A items of your choice
Category B items of your choice

Roasted Potato Wedges   **Category: B**   **Serves: 4-6**

You can add any other herbs or spices to your liking, including cumin, chili powder, rosemary, chives or parsley.

7 large russet baking potatoes
3/4 cup olive oil, divided
2 1/2 teaspoons seasoned salt
1 tablespoon dried oregano
1 tablespoon dried basil
1 teaspoon pepper

Preheat oven to 425°.

Scrub potatoes, cut in half lengthwise and slice halves into steak fries. Place in a large bowl and toss with 1/2 cup of olive oil and spices until well coated.

Place potatoes on a rimmed baking sheet, drizzle excess oil and spices from bowl over potatoes, and roast for 25 minutes. Remove pan from oven, gently turn potatoes over with a spatula, drizzle with additional 1/4 cup olive oil and return to oven. Roast for another 20-25 minutes or until potatoes are tender, nicely browned and crisp.

Sprinkle with additional seasoned salt and pepper if desired. Serve with ketchup, barbecue sauce or sour cream.

Serve with:
Tossed salad
Category A items of your choice
Category B items of your choice

Sweet Potato Fries   **Category: B**   **Serves: 4-6**

What a delicious alternative to traditional French fries!

6 medium sweet potatoes or yams
3/4 cup olive oil, divided
2 teaspoons salt
1/2 teaspoon pepper
1 teaspoon ground cumin
1 teaspoon chili powder
Maple syrup

Preheat oven to 425°.

Scrub potatoes, cut in half lengthwise and slice halves into steak fries. Place in a large bowl and toss with 1/2 cup of olive oil and spices until well coated.

Place potatoes on a rimmed baking sheet, drizzle excess oil and spices from bowl over potatoes, and roast for 25 minutes. Remove pan from oven, gently turn potatoes over with a spatula, drizzle with additional 1/4 cup olive oil and return to oven. Roast for another 20-25 minutes or until potatoes are tender, nicely browned and slightly crisp.

Sprinkle with additional salt and pepper if desired. Serve with maple syrup for dipping.

Serve with:
Tossed salad
Category A items of your choice
Category B items of your choice

Summer Squash Sauté   **Category: A/C**   **Serves: 3-4**

A tasty way to take advantage of summer squash when they're plentiful and fresh.

3 small zucchini squash
3 small yellow squash
4 cloves garlic, minced
1-14 oz. can diced tomatoes (drained)
1/4 cup olive oil
1/2 cup grated Parmesan or Romano cheese
1/2 teaspoon salt

Wash squashes and slice into 1/4" rounds.

Heat olive oil in a large skillet over medium heat. Sauté garlic briefly until fragrant but not browned.

Add squash slices and salt and sauté until crisp-tender, being careful not to overcook, as the squash can quickly turn mushy.

Remove from heat and transfer to serving bowl. Toss with cheese and tomatoes. Serve at once.

Note: Leftovers are delicious additions to omelets.

Serve with:
Category A items of your choice, and
Category B items of your choice (for optimal digestion, you may need to omit the cheese or substitute soy cheese) **OR**
Category C items of your choice

Not the Spinach You Grew Up With   Category: A/C   Serves: 3-4

Sadly, I grew up hating spinach because it was cooked to death and tasted like green mush with butter. If only I had known then how delicious it could be! My 9 year-old son loves this dish.

1 1/2 lbs. fresh spinach leaves (preferably baby spinach if you can find it)
3 tablespoons water
3 tablespoons olive oil
1/4 cup shredded Parmesan or Romano cheese
Salt and freshly ground black pepper to taste

Thoroughly wash spinach (if not using pre-washed). Drain thoroughly.

Place water, then spinach into a Dutch oven or large saucepan. Cover and steam over medium heat until just barely wilted, about 2-3 minutes.

Remove from pan with a fork (to drain off excess water) and place in serving bowl. Drizzle with olive oil, sprinkle with cheese and add salt and pepper to taste.

Serve with:
Category A items of your choice, and
Category B items of your choice (for optimal digestion, you may need to omit the cheese or substitute soy cheese) **OR**
Category C items of your choice (Chicken or fish go well)

Uncandied Sweet Potatoes   **Category: B**   **Serves: 6-8**

This is a truly unique sweet potato recipe—there's plenty of delicious flavor here without it ending up being more of a dessert than a vegetable dish.

6 sweet potatoes or yams
2 tablespoons olive oil
2 tablespoons molasses
2 tablespoons honey
2 tablespoons maple syrup
1 tablespoon cinnamon

Peel sweet potatoes or yams and cut into 1/2" slices or chunks (or a little of both). Place in a large Dutch oven or saucepot with enough water to cover. Cover, bring to a boil and cook until just barely tender; drain.

Preheat oven to 350°.

Turn potatoes into a casserole or baking dish. Drizzle olive oil, molasses, honey and maple syrup over potatoes, then sprinkle with cinnamon. Stir to combine.

Bake uncovered for 20 minutes. Remove from oven, stir potatoes well, adding a bit more olive oil if they appear dry, and additional cinnamon if desired.

Return to oven and bake another 15 minutes or until potatoes are nicely browned and tender.

Serve with:
Sherry's Garlic Green Beans
Tossed salad
Category A items of your choice
Category B items of your choice

Stuffed Potatoes   **Category: B**   **Serves: 6**

These are a wonderfully delicious alternative to the same-old twice-baked potatoes with cheese and bacon bits, and kids LOVE them!

6 large russet baking potatoes
1 medium butternut squash
2/3 cup melted butter or Earth Balance
1 teaspoon seasoned salt
1/2 teaspoon ground cumin
2 tablespoons maple syrup
Olive oil for brushing
Paprika for sprinkling

Preheat oven to 425°. Scrub potatoes, pierce with a fork and bake in oven until soft, about 60-70 minutes.

Peel squash, cut in half and remove seeds, then cut into small cubes. Cook in boiling water for 20-25 minutes or until soft. Remove from heat, drain, return to pan and mash with a potato masher. Measure out 2 1/4 cups of mashed squash and set aside.

When potatoes are done, remove from oven, cool slightly, cut in half lengthwise and scoop out pulp, being careful not to tear the skin. Mash potato pulp until smooth, then add 2 1/4 cups mashed squash, melted butter, salt, cumin and maple syrup, stirring until well-mixed.

Raise oven heat to broil setting. Refill potato shells with potato-squash mixture (it will heap over the tops of the shells). Brush with olive oil, sprinkle with paprika, put on a baking sheet and broil for 5-7 minutes or until lightly browned.

Serve with:
Sherry's Peas and Carrots
Tossed salad
Category A or Category B items of your choice

Sautéed Broccoli Rabe (Rappi)   **Category: A/C**   **Serves: 3-4**

If you can't find broccoli rabe, mustard greens or Swiss chard also work well in this recipe.

2 lbs. broccoli rabe (rappi)
4 cloves garlic, thinly sliced
1/2 cup olive oil
1 teaspoon salt
1/2 cup Parmesan or Romano cheese

Cut off tough 1" of bottoms of rabe stems and rinse broccoli rabe thoroughly.

Heat olive oil in a large skillet and add garlic, sautéing until fragrant but not browned.

Add broccoli rabe, cover and cook, stirring occasionally, until rabe is tender.

Remove from heat, toss with salt and cheese and serve.

Serve with:
Category A items of your choice, and
Category B items of your choice (for optimal digestion, you may need to omit the cheese or substitute soy cheese) **OR**
Category C items of your choice (Italian sausage, beef or fish all go well)

Yellow Squash with Basil   **Category: A**   **Serves: 4-5**

This is delicious either hot or at room temperature.

4 tablespoons olive oil, divided
1 1/2 lbs. yellow squash
3 garlic cloves, minced
1/4 teaspoon salt
1/8 teaspoon freshly ground black pepper
1/4 cup chopped fresh basil

Wash squash, slice in half lengthwise and cut crosswise into 1/8" thick slices.

Heat 2 tablespoons of the oil in a large skillet over medium-high heat. Add half of the squash and sauté until browned but not mushy (about 5 minutes). Transfer squash to a large bowl. Heat remaining 2 tablespoons olive oil and cook remaining squash in the same manner. Add second batch of squash to bowl.

Add garlic to skillet and sauté over medium heat until fragrant but not browned. Return squash to pan, add salt, pepper and basil, and cook and toss until well-combined.

Remove from heat, transfer to serving bowl.

Serve with:
Category A items of your choice, and
Category B items of your choice **OR**
Category C items of your choice (Steak or pork go well)

Spaghetti Squash and Tomatoes   **Category: B**   **Serves: 3-4**

This can be a meal in itself!

1 spaghetti squash
1 medium onion, chopped
1 small green bell pepper, chopped
2 cloves garlic, chopped
2 tablespoons olive oil
4 medium tomatoes, chopped (or use 2-15oz. cans diced tomatoes, undrained)
1/2 teaspoon salt
1/2 teaspoon dried oregano
1/4 cup fresh basil, chopped
1/8 teaspoon pepper
2 tablespoons butter or Earth Balance
Salt and pepper to taste

Preheat oven to 375°.

Pierce the squash shell several times with a fork and place in baking dish. Cook for 1 to 1 1/2 hours (depending on size of squash). Cool for 10-15 minutes.

While squash bakes, cook onion, green pepper and garlic in oil in saucepan over medium heat for about 5 minutes, stirring occasionally until onion and pepper are tender. Stir in tomatoes, salt, oregano, basil and pepper. Bring to a boil, lower heat and simmer uncovered, stirring occasionally, for 10 minutes.

Cut baked and slightly cooled squash in half lengthwise; remove seeds and fibrous strings. Pull a fork through the squash halves lengthwise to separate it into long strands (like spaghetti) and place strands in a bowl. Toss with butter and add salt and pepper to taste.

Spoon tomato mixture over squash and serve, passing additional tomato mixture if desired.

<u>Serve with:</u>
Tossed salad
Category A items of your choice
Category B items of your choice

Asparagus with Pine Nuts and Balsamic Vinegar   **Serves: 2-3**
Category: A

What a nice change from ho-hum asparagus with butter or hollandaise sauce.

1 lb. fresh asparagus
2 tablespoons pine nuts, toasted
3 tablespoons butter or Earth Balance
1 teaspoon balsamic vinegar
Salt and pepper to taste

Preheat oven to 350°. Spread pine nuts on a baking sheet and toast in oven for 5-10 minutes or until golden.

Wash the asparagus and trim off the tough end of the stems. Cook spears in a small amount of boiling water for 3-5 minutes, just until tender.

Drain asparagus and return to pan. Toss with butter and vinegar, add salt and pepper to taste.

Place in serving bowl, sprinkle pine nuts over and serve.

Serve with:
Category A items of your choice, and
Category B items of your choice **OR**
Category C items of your choice (Steak or fish go well)

Green Beans Almondine   **Category: A**   **Serves: 6**

An easy, elegant side dish.

2 lbs. green beans
1/3 cup olive oil
1/8 teaspoon almond extract
1/2 cup slivered almonds
Dash salt and pepper

Preheat oven to 350°.

Steam green beans until tender. Drain, return to pot and set aside.

In a small bowl, combine oil, almond extract, salt and pepper. Pour over beans and toss to combine.

Place almond slivers on a baking sheet and toast in oven for 10 minutes or until golden brown. Watch closely so that they don't burn.

Toss almonds with beans and oil. Place in serving dish and serve at once.

<u>Serve with:</u>
Category A items of your choice, and
Category B items of your choice **OR**
Category C items of your choice (Beef, chicken or fish all go well)

Garlic Roasted Potatoes   **Category: B**   **Serves: 4-6**

2 1/2 pounds red or golden potatoes, scrubbed and cubed
8 cloves garlic, pressed
1/2 cup olive oil
1 tablespoon lemon juice
1 tablespoon paprika
4 teaspoons rosemary leaves, crushed
1 teaspoon salt
1 teaspoon pepper

Preheat oven to 375°.

Heat oil in a small saucepan over medium heat. Add garlic and sauté until fragrant but not browned.
Stir in lemon juice, paprika, rosemary, salt and pepper; remove from heat.

Place potatoes in a large bowl. Pour garlic-oil mixture over potatoes and toss to coat well.

Spread potatoes in a single layer into a large roasting or baking pan. Bake until golden brown and crisp,
about 1 hour, turning and stirring every 20 minutes.

Serve with:
Tossed salad
Category A items of your choice
Category B items of your choice

Snacks and Entertaining

Eggnog   **Category: Dessert**   **Serves: 12-15**

It's tempting to go to the dairy section and buy this in a carton, but homemade is SO much better. Make this and you will be the hit of the holiday party!

13 large eggs at room temperature
3/4 cup sugar, divided
1 cup bourbon whiskey
1/2 cup rum
1 1/2 cups milk
2 cups heavy cream
Ground nutmeg for garnish

Separate eggs and place in 2 large mixing bowls. Add 6 tablespoons sugar to each bowl. Beat egg yolks and sugar until thick and deep yellow. Add brandy, rum and milk and stir well; pour mixture into punch bowl.

Beat egg whites and sugar until stiff peaks form; fold into yolk mixture. Whip cream for 30 seconds or until slightly thickened; fold into yolk and white mixture.

Sprinkle with nutmeg for garnish, if desired.

Serve with:
Similar to a dessert, eggnog is a mixture of proteins and starch. Eggnog should be consumed in moderation, preferably with a properly combined raw vegetable appetizer.

Spinach Bread   **Category: B**   **Serves: 12-15**

This uses the same filling as Spanakopita. To save time, substitute frozen chopped spinach, thawed and squeezed dry, for the fresh spinach.

1-1 lb. bag fresh pizza dough
2 lbs. spinach
1/2 lb. feta cheese, crumbled
1-16oz. carton ricotta cheese
4 cloves garlic, minced
3 green onions, thinly sliced
2 tablespoons olive oil
1/2 cup chopped fresh parsley
1 tsp. garlic salt
Olive oil as needed

Preheat oven to 375°.

Steam spinach just until wilted; drain, squeeze dry and chop. Sauté garlic and green onions in olive oil until garlic is fragrant but not browned; remove from heat. Combine spinach, feta, ricotta, garlic, onions and oil from sauté pan, parsley and garlic salt in a large mixing bowl; stir until well mixed.

Roll dough out into a large rectangle (about 12" x 15"). Spread filling over dough, leaving about 3/4" border around the edges. Gently fold dough and filling over the long way into thirds; pinch seam and edges tightly to keep filling from seeping out while baking.

Using 2 spatulas, transfer bread onto a lightly greased jelly roll pan. Bake for 25-30 minutes, or until nicely browned. Cool on rack, then cut into 1" slices.

Note: For optimal digestion, you may need to omit cheese or substitute soy cheese.

Hummus   **Category: B**   **Makes: 3-1/2 cups**

People differ in how lemony or salty they like their hummus, so I use a "taste and see" approach in my recipe.

3 cloves garlic, minced
1/2 cup fresh parsley
2 green onions, sliced
2-15 oz. cans garbanzo beans (chick peas), drained and rinsed
6 tablespoons tahini (sesame spread)
1/2 teaspoon salt
1/2 teaspoon ground cumin
1/2 cup water, plus more if necessary
1-3 tablespoons fresh lemon juice (depending on your preference)

Place first 8 ingredients, and 1 tablespoon of the lemon juice in food processor or blender. Puree until smooth. Taste and add second and third tablespoons of lemon juice and/or additional salt, if desired. If hummus seems too thick, stir in additional water 1 tablespoon at a time until desired consistency.

Serve with:
Vegetable dippers (cut up carrots, celery, cucumbers, broccoli, cauliflower, radishes, bell peppers)
Pita bread triangles
Bread cubes
Tortilla chips

Bruschetta   **Category: B**   **Makes: 40 pieces**

A little messy to serve, but so delicious (and healthy)! Be sure to have paper plates and napkins handy.

Tomato mixture:
8 ripe plum tomatoes, seeded and diced
2 tablespoons minced garlic
1/2 cup chopped fresh basil leaves
1/4 cup chopped fresh parsley
2 teaspoons fresh lemon juice
1 tablespoon olive oil
Salt and freshly ground black pepper to taste

2 baguettes, cut in 1/2" slices
6-7 cloves garlic, peeled and halved

In a bowl, combine tomato mixture ingredients; mix well and set aside for at least 2-3 hours. (Do not refrigerate.)

Preheat oven to 350°.

Place bread slices on baking sheets and toast in oven until lightly browned. Remove from oven, rub each slice with cut side of garlic halves and place on a platter.

Invite guests to spoon tomato mixture over bread slices as desired.

Black Bean Dip   **Category: B**   **Makes: 2 cups**

A nice, spicy addition to an assortment of party appetizers.

1-16 oz. can black beans
1 1/2 teaspoons ground cumin
1/2 teaspoon ground coriander
Pinch of cayenne pepper
1 garlic clove, pressed
2/3 cup chopped fresh parsley
2/3 cup salsa
1 tablespoon olive oil
1 teaspoon fresh lemon juice
Salt to taste

Rinse and drain the beans, place them in a bowl and mash well with a fork.

Stir in the cumin, coriander, cayenne, garlic, parsley, salsa, olive oil and lemon juice; mix thoroughly.
Add salt to taste.

Serve with:
Vegetable dippers (cut up carrots, celery, cucumbers, broccoli, cauliflower, radishes, bell peppers)
Pita bread triangles
Bread cubes
Tortilla chips

Vodka Punch   **Category: Dessert**   **Serves: 12-15**

A classic for a ladies' party or luncheon.

2-6 oz. cans of orange juice, undiluted
2-6 oz. cans of lemonade, undiluted
1 quart chilled ginger ale
2 cups chilled cranberry juice cocktail
2 cups vodka
1 pint lime sherbet for garnish (optional)
1 quart chilled club soda

Mix all ingredients except lime sherbet in punch bowl. Just before serving, drop lime sherbet in dollops on top if desired.

Irish Cream   **Category: C**   **Serves: 8-10**

Much more economical that buying the liquor store brand, and just as delicious.

1 cup light cream
1-14 oz. can sweetened condensed milk
1 3/4 cups whiskey
4 eggs
1 teaspoon vanilla
1/2 teaspoon almond extract
2 tablespoons chocolate syrup
1 tablespoon instant coffee granules

Place all ingredients in a blender and process until well mixed. Serve at room temperature or over ice.

Desserts

Most foods that people consider to be desserts contain mixtures of starches, proteins and sometimes fruit. As a result, they don't digest easily or comfortably. However, most people do like a sweet treat now and then. So for those people who "can't live without" desserts, most can eat them once in a while and still live completely free of stomach pain. Just remember that moderation is the key!

Ideally, all desserts should be eaten under the following guidelines:

1) Have dessert only on a rare or special occasion— for instance, a birthday, anniversary or holiday—once per month or less
2) Have a small serving or share it with someone—less is best
3) Wait as long as possible (preferably 3 hours or more) after a properly combined meal
4) Make sure your next two meals are at least 50% high water content foods to help cleanse your system

Dutch Apple Pie   **Category: Dessert**   **Serves: 10-12**

A good, old-fashioned favorite.

Crust:
1 single crust pie shell, unbaked (for homemade crust, see recipe on p. 157)

Filling:
8 large Cortland or other tart apples, peeled and sliced thin
1 cup sugar
1 tablespoon cinnamon

Crumb Topping:
1/3 cup sugar
3/4 cup flour
6 tablespoons butter

Preheat oven to 425°. Roll out pie crust and place in a deep 10" pie pan; crimp edges..

Combine apples, sugar and cinnamon in a large bowl; toss and stir until well mixed and a juice starts to form. Turn into pie shell with a slotted spoon to drain some of the juices and prevent the filling from becoming too watery.

In a medium sized bowl, combine sugar and flour. Cut in butter with a pastry blender or two forks until well combined. Sprinkle evenly over apples.

Bake at 425° for 15 minutes, reduce heat to 350° and continue baking for 45 minutes or until crust is browned and apples are tender.

Serve with:
All desserts, especially fruit-based desserts, should be eaten either on an empty stomach or at least 3 hours after a properly combined meal.

Traditional Apple Pie   **Category: Dessert**   **Serves: 10-12**

Like its cousin, Dutch Apple Pie, this is definitely a crowd-pleaser.

Crust:
1 double-crust pie shell, unbaked (for homemade crust, see recipe on p. 157)

Filling:
8 large Cortland or other tart apples, peeled and sliced thin
1 cup sugar
1 tablespoon cinnamon

Topping:
1-2 tablespoons milk
1 tablespoon sugar

Preheat oven to 425°. Roll out pie crusts and place one in a deep 10" pie pan.

Combine apples, sugar and cinnamon in a large bowl; toss and stir until well mixed and a juice starts to form. Turn into pie shell with a slotted spoon to drain some of the juices and prevent the filling from becoming too watery.

Place second pie crust on top of apples; pinch together edges of bottom and top crusts to seal. Brush milk over top crust and with pastry brush. Sprinkle with sugar and make holes in the top with a fork so steam can escape.

Bake at 425° for 15 minutes, reduce heat to 350° and continue baking for 45 minutes or until crust is browned and apples are tender.

Serve with:
All desserts, especially fruit-based desserts, should be eaten either on an empty stomach or at least 3 hours after a properly combined meal.

Congo Bars   **Category: Dessert**   **Makes: 4 dozen**

Bring these to a party or get-together and watch them disappear!

2/3 cup melted butter or Earth Balance
1-1 lb. box light brown sugar
3 eggs
2 2/3 cups flour
2 1/2 teaspoons baking powder
1/2 teaspoon salt
1-12 oz. package semi-sweet chocolate chips

Combine flour, baking powder and salt in a medium bowl; set aside. Melt butter and set aside.

Combine brown sugar and eggs; beat well with electric mixer. Gradually add flour mixture alternatively with melted butter, beating well after each addition. Stir in chocolate chips.

Spread mixture into a large jelly roll pan (approximately 18" x 12"). Bake at 350° for 25 minutes, or until golden brown and set.

Cool in pan and cut into bars or squares.

<u>Serve with:</u>
All desserts should be eaten either on an empty stomach or at least 3 hours after a properly combined meal.

Chocolate Custard Pie   **Category: Dessert**   **Serves: 10-12**

So rich and creamy that you'll never used boxed or canned pudding again!

Crust:
1 single crust pie shell, baked and cooled (for homemade crust, see recipe on p. 157)

Filling:
1 cup sugar
1/4 cup cornstarch
1/4 teaspoon salt
3 cups milk
3 egg yolks
2 tablespoons butter
2 teaspoons vanilla extract
2 squares unsweetened chocolate

Combine sugar, cornstarch and salt in a medium saucepan. Stir in milk and blend until smooth. Add chocolate, place pan onto stove and heat over medium heat. Bring to a boil, stirring constantly.

Remove from heat. In a small bowl, beat egg yolks then gradually stir a small amount of heated mixture into eggs. Pour egg mixture into saucepan, mixing well.

Bring mixture to a boil, stir in butter and vanilla. Cool with plastic wrap on top of filling to prevent the formation of a "skin;" pour into baked pie shell. Chill several hours or overnight.

Serve with:
All desserts should be eaten either on an empty stomach or at least 3 hours after a properly combined meal.

Easy and Delicious Pie Crust   **Category: B**   **Makes: 4 single or 2 double crusts**

Store-bought pie shells are OK in a pinch, but this homemade recipe is so easy and the taste is definitely worth a little extra effort.

3 cups unbleached flour
1 teaspoon salt
1 1/2 cups shortening (I use Earth Balance shortening as a healthy alternative—it has no hydrogenated oils)
1 egg
1 tablespoon vinegar
5 tablespoons ice water

Combine flour and salt in a large bowl. Cut in shortening with a pastry blender or two forks until mixture is crumbly. Beat egg, vinegar and water in a small bowl; pour into flour mixture and stir until well-blended. Using hands, divide dough into 4 balls.

Roll out dough on well-floured work surface, adding a little extra flour if the dough seems sticky. Place in pie or quiche pan as needed.

Unused dough balls may be refrigerated for 2 weeks, or frozen for up to 3 months. Be sure to wrap well in plastic wrap.

To bake a one-crust pie shell: Preheat oven to 400°. Roll out crust and place into the pie plate; flute the edge. Prick the bottom and sides of the crust with a fork.

Place a piece of parchment paper the size of the pie plate inside the pie shell, then place pie weights or dried beans on the bottom. (This helps the shell to retain its shape.) Bake shell for 5 minutes, remove weights or beans and parchment, then return to oven and bake another 3-5 minutes or until golden brown.

Mike's Favorite Pecan Pie   **Category: Dessert**   **Serves: 8-10**

My husband Mike <u>loves</u> pecan pie, so this is a staple for Thanksgiving every year.

Crust:
1 single crust pie shell, unbaked (for homemade crust, see recipe on p. 157)

Filling:
1 cup sugar
3 large eggs
1/2 cup light corn syrup
3 tablespoons butter or Earth Balance, melted
2 teaspoons vanilla
1 3/4 cups chopped pecans

Preheat oven to 350°.

Roll out pie crust and place in 9" pie pan.

Whisk first 5 filling ingredients together in a medium bowl until well-blended. Stir in 3/4 cup of the pecans. Pour into prepared crust. Sprinkle with remaining 1 cup pecans.

Bake 1 hour and 15 minutes or until set. Cool thoroughly before serving.

<u>Serve with:</u>
All desserts should be eaten either on an empty stomach or at least 3 hours after a properly combined meal.

Sweet Potato Pie   **Category: Dessert**   **Serves: 8-10**

This is a different twist on the usual favorite pumpkin pie. The filling is very creamy and the pie slices beautifully.

Crust:
1 single crust pie shell, unbaked (for homemade crust, see recipe on p. 157)

Filling:
1/3 cup butter or Earth Balance, softened
1/2 cup sugar
2 eggs, lightly beaten
3/4 cup evaporated milk
2 cups mashed sweet potatoes
1 teaspoon vanilla
1/2 teaspoon ground cinnamon
1/2 teaspoon nutmeg
1/4 teaspoon salt

Preheat oven to 425°.

Roll out pie crust and place in 9" pie pan.

In a mixing bowl, cream butter and sugar. Add eggs; mix well. Add milk, sweet potatoes, vanilla, cinnamon, nutmeg and salt; mix well. Pour into pie shell.

Bake at 425° for 15 minutes. Reduce heat to 350° and bake 35-40 minutes longer or until a knife inserted near center comes out clean. Cool thoroughly before serving.

Serve with:
All desserts should be eaten either on an empty stomach or at least 3 hours after a properly combined meal.

Raspberry Bars   **Category: Dessert**   **Makes: 16**

These are easy and so delicious.

2 1/4 cups flour
1 cup sugar
1 cup butter or Earth Balance, softened
1 egg
1-10oz. jar raspberry preserves

Preheat oven to 350°.

In large mixing bowl, combine flour, sugar, butter and egg. Beat at low speed of electric mixer until mixture is well combined and crumbly.

Reserve 1/2 cup crumb mixture. Press remaining crumb mixture into bottom of an 8" x 8" square baking pan.

Spread preserves over crumb mixture to within 1/4 inch of edge. Sprinkle remaining crumb mixture over preserves.

Bake 40-45 minutes or until topping is browned. Cool and cut into 16 squares, 2"x 2" each.

Serve with:
All desserts should be eaten either on an empty stomach or at least 3 hours after a properly combined meal.

The Best Brownies Ever   **Category: Dessert**   **Makes: 3 dozen**

I've sampled a lot of brownie varieties, but this one seems to be everyone's favorite.

1 cup butter or Earth Balance, melted
2 cups sugar
2 teaspoons vanilla
4 eggs
3/4 cup unsweetened cocoa powder
1 cup unbleached flour
1/2 teaspoon baking powder
1/4 teaspoon salt
1 cup chopped nuts (optional)

Preheat oven to 350°. Grease a 13"x 9"x 2" baking pan with shortening. (I use Earth Balance shortening, as it has no hydrogenated oils.)

In a large mixing bowl, combine butter, sugar and vanilla. Add eggs one at a time, beating well with a wooden spoon after each addition. Add cocoa and beat well until blended. Add flour, baking powder and salt; beat well. Stir in nuts if using.

Pour batter into prepared pan. Bake for 30-35 minutes. Cool and cut into bars.

Serve with:
All desserts should be eaten either on an empty stomach or at least 3 hours after a properly combined meal.

The World's Best Carrot Cake   **Category: Dessert**   **Serves: 16**

When my husband Mike and I were planning to get married, we decided we wanted carrot cake for our wedding cake. Mike made me tell the bakery how I make my cake so they could duplicate it for our wedding!

1 1/2 cups canola oil
2 cups sugar
3 eggs
2 cups unbleached flour
2 teaspoons cinnamon
2 teaspoons baking soda
1 teaspoon salt
1-7oz. bag shredded coconut
1-8 oz. can crushed pineapple packed in juice, undrained
2 teaspoons vanilla
2 cups shredded carrots
1 cup chopped nuts (optional)

Preheat oven to 350°. Grease and flour a 13"x 9"x 2" inch baking pan.

Mix oil and sugar in large bowl. Add eggs, beating well. In a separate bowl, sift flour, cinnamon, baking soda and salt. Add to beaten mixture. Fold in remaining ingredients. Pour into prepared pan and bake for 45-50 minutes or until a toothpick inserted in center comes out clean.

Cream Cheese Frosting:
4 tablespoons butter or Earth Balance
8 oz. cream cheese, softened
2 teaspoons vanilla
1-1 lb. box confectioner's sugar

Beat all ingredients until smooth. Spread over cooled carrot cake.

<u>Serve with:</u>
All desserts should be eaten either on an empty stomach or at least 3 hours after a properly combined meal.

Black Magic Cake   **Category: Dessert**   **Serves: 16**

A very dense, moist chocolate cake.

2 cups sugar
1 3/4 cups unbleached flour
3/4 cup unsweetened cocoa powder
2 teaspoons baking soda
1 teaspoon baking powder
1 teaspoon salt
2 eggs
1 cup strong black coffee
1 cup buttermilk
1/2 cup canola oil
1 teaspoon vanilla

Preheat oven to 350º.

Grease and flour 13"x 9"x 2" baking pan.

In large mixer bowl blend sugar, flour, cocoa, baking soda, baking powder and salt. Add eggs, coffee, buttermilk, oil and vanilla; beat on medium speed with electric mixer for 2 minutes (batter will be thin.) Pour into prepared pan.

Bake 35 to 40 minutes, or until cake springs back when lightly touched.

Cool and top with your favorite frosting, or dust with confectioner's sugar.

Serve with:
All desserts should be eaten either on an empty stomach or at least 3 hours after a properly combined meal.

Index- Alphabetical

A

Asparagus Soup	61
Asparagus with Pine Nuts and Balsamic Vinegar	138

B

Basil Pesto	34
Beans, Green Almondine	139
Black Bean Chili	114
Black Bean Dip	147
Black Bean Soup	53
Black Magic Cake	164
Blueberry Muffins	15
Borscht	51
Bowties and Broccoli	68
Bread, Boston Brown	21
Bread, Corn	19
Bread, Orange-Cranberry	20
Bread, Pumpkin	25
Bread, Spinach	144
Bread, Zucchini	24

Breakfast Fritatta   16

Breakfast Smoothies   18

Broccoli & Swiss Cheese Quiche   70

Broccoli Rabe, Sautéed   134

Broccoli with Garlic and Cheese   125

Brownies   161

Bruschetta   146

Bubble & Squeak (Fried Potatoes and Cabbage)   117

Burritos, Corn   109

C

Cabbage, and Potatoes, Fried   117

Cabbage, Polish Stuffed   84

Cabbage, Polish Style   122

Caesar Salad   41

Cake, Carrot   162

Cake, Chocolate   164

Carrot And Cilantro Soup   64

Cauliflower, Italian   121

Chili, Black Bean   114

Chili, Vegetarian   83

Chili, Vegetarian with Bulgur Wheat   103

Chocolate Custard Pie   156

Coci Helen's Salad Dressing   31

Cod with Dill Sauce   110

Congo Bars   155

Corn Bread   19

Corn Burritos	109
Corn Chowder	58
Corn Fritters	78
Cream of Mushroom Soup	62

D

Delicious Panfried Fish	87
Diced Vegetable Salad	47
Dip, Black Bean	147
Dressing, Buttermilk	31
Dressing, French	30
Dressing, Honey Mustard	38
Dressing, Thousand Island	29
Dutch Apple Pie	153

E

Easy and Delicious Pie Crust	157
Easy Homemade Pickles	35
Eggnog	143
Eggplant Lasagna	115
Eggplant Parmesan	74

F

Feta and Tomato Shrimp Scampi	108
Fish, Delicious Panfried	87
Freida's Kapusta	122
Fresh Salsa	32

Fritatta   16
Fritters, Corn   78
Fruit Salad   42

G

Garlic Roasted Potatoes   140
Golabki (Polish Stuffed Cabbage)   84
Greek Baked Vegetables   93
Greek Salad   44
Green Beans Almondine   139
Green Beans, Sherry's with Garlic   123
Greens and Beans   86

H

Honey Mustard Vinaigrette   38
Hummus   145

I

Irish Cream   149
Italian Butter (Bread Dipping Oil)   36
Italian Cauliflower   121
Italian Potato Salad   45

L

Lasagna with Meat   81
Lasagna with Vegetables   79
Lasagna, Eggplant   115

Lentil Soup   52
Liana's Homemade Pizza   94

M

Marinade, Teriyaki   37
Mike's Favorite Pecan Pie   158
Minestrone Soup   59
Mom's Buttermilk Pancakes   22
Muffins, Blueberry   15
Muffins, Pumpkin-Apple   23

N

Nancy's Boston Brown Bread   21
Not the Spinach You Grew Up With   131

O

Oil, Bread Dipping   36
Orange-Cranberry Bread   20

P

Pan Bagnat   102
Pancakes, Buttermilk   22
Pancakes, Potato   96
Parsley Pesto   33
Pasta E Fagioli   56
Pasta, Bowties and Broccoli   68
Pasta, Spaghetti Puttanesca   101

Pasta, Sundried Tomato   69
Peas and Carrots, Sherry's   124
Peppers, Stuffed   88
Pesto, Basil   34
Pesto, Parsley   33
Pickles, Easy Homemade   35
Pie Crust   157
Pie, Chocolate Custard   156
Pie, Dutch Apple   153
Pie, Pecan   158
Pie, Sweet Potato   159
Pie, Traditional Apple   154
Pizza Dough   94
Pizza, Liana's Homemade   94
Pizza, Tomato and Goat Cheese   95
Potato Pancakes   96
Potato Wedges, Roasted   128
Potatoes, and Cabbage, Fried   117
Potatoes, Garlic Roasted   140
Potatoes, Roasted Garlic Mashed   127
Potatoes, Stuffed   133
Potatoes, Sweet, Fries   129
Potatoes, Yummy Fried   126
Pumpkin Bread   25
Pumpkin-Apple Muffins   23

Q

Quiche, Broccoli & Swiss	70
Quiche, Spinach & Feta Cheese	71

R

Rappi, Sautéed	134
Raspberry Bars	160
Ratatouille	76
Red Lentil Stew	99
Rice, Spanish	90
Rice, Spicy With Red Beans	113
Roasted Garlic Mashed Potatoes	127
Roasted Potato Wedges	128

S

Salad, Caesar	41
Salad, Diced Vegetable	47
Salad, Fruit	42
Salad, Greek	44
Salad, Italian Potato	45
Salad, Spinach and Roasted Garlic	46
Salmon With Brown Sugar Glaze	92
Salmon With Horseradish Sauce	98
Salmon with Raspberry Sauce	111
Salsa, Tomato	32
Sautéed Broccoli Rabe (Rappi)	134
Sea Bass with Feta	112

Seafood Stew 105

Sherry Brescia's Outrageously Delicious Spaghetti Sauce 67

Sherry's Garlic Green Beans 123

Sherry's Peas and Carrots 124

Shrimp Scampi 91

Shrimp With Basil-Garlic Sauce 97

Shrimp, Feta and Tomato Scampi 108

Smoothies, Breakfast 18

Smoothies, Fruit 18

Soup, Asparagus 61

Soup, Black Bean 53

Soup, Carrot and Cilantro 64

Soup, Cream of Mushroom 62

Soup, Lentil 52

Soup, Minestrone 59

Soup, Pasta and Bean 56

Soup, Tomato with Basil 63

Soup, Winter Vegetable 54

Spaghetti Puttanesca 101

Spaghetti Sauce 67

Spaghetti Squash and Tomatoes 136

Spanakopita 72

Spanish Rice 90

Spicy French Dressing 30

Spicy Red Beans and Rice 113

Spinach & Feta Cheese Quiche 71

Spinach and Roasted Garlic Salad 46

Spinach Bread   144
Spinach, Not What You Grew Up With   131
Squash, Spaghetti and Tomatoes   136
Squash, Yellow with Basil   135
Squash, Yellow, Summer Squash Sauté   130
Stew, Red Lentil   99
Stew, Seafood   105
Stew, Tangy Vegetable   107
Stuffed Peppers   88
Stuffed Potatoes   133
Summer Squash Sauté   130
Sundried Tomato Pasta   69
Sweet Potato Fries   129
Sweet Potato Pie   159
Sweet Potatoes, Uncandied   132

T

Tabouli   48
Tangy Vegetable Stew   107
Teriyaki Marinade   37
The Best Brownies Ever   161
The Best Thousand Island Salad Dressing   29
The World's Best Carrot Cake   162
Tomato and Goat Cheese Pizza   95
Tomato Soup With Basil   63
Traditional Apple Pie   154

U

Uncandied Sweet Potatoes   132

V

Vegetables, Greek Baked   93
Vegetarian Chili   83
Vegetarian Chili with Bulgur Wheat   103
Vodka Punch   148

W

Winter Vegetable Soup   54

Y

Yellow Squash with Basil   135
Yummy Fried Potatoes   126

Z

Zucchini Bread   24
Zucchini, Summer Squash Sauté   130

Index- by Category

Category A--High Water Content Vegetables

Asparagus Soup	61
Asparagus with Pine Nuts and Balsamic Vinegar	138
Freida's Kapusta	122
Green Beans Almondine	139
Ratatouille	76
Sherry Brescia's Outrageously Delicious Spaghetti Sauce	67
Sherry's Garlic Green Beans	123
Tomato Soup With Basil	63
Yellow Squash with Basil	135

Category A/C--High Water Content Vegetables with some Protein

Note: These may be converted to Category A by omitting cheese

Broccoli with Garlic and Cheese	125
Caesar Salad	41
Diced Vegetable Salad	47
Greek Salad	44
Italian Cauliflower	121
Not the Spinach You Grew Up With	131
Sautéed Broccoli Rabe	134
Spinach and Roasted Garlic Salad	46

Summer Squash Sauté   130

Category B--Starches
Black Bean Chili   114
Black Bean Dip   147
Black Bean Soup   53
Blueberry Muffins   15
Borscht   51
Bowties and Broccoli   68
Bruschetta   146
Bubble & Squeak   117
Carrot and Cilantro Soup   64
Corn Bread   19
Corn Burritos   109
Corn Chowder   58
Corn Fritters   78
Cream of Mushroom Soup   62
Easy and Delicious Pie Crust   157
Eggplant Parmesan   74
Garlic Roasted Potatoes   140
Golabki (Polish Stuffed Cabbage)   84
Greek Baked Vegetables   93
Greens and Beans   86
Hummus   145
Italian Potato Salad   45
Lasagna with Meat   81
Lasagna with Vegetables   79
Lentil Soup   52
Liana's Homemade Pizza   94

Minestrone Soup	59
Mom's Buttermilk Pancakes	22
Nancy's Boston Brown Bread	21
Orange-Cranberry Bread	20
Pan Bagnat	102
Pasta E. Faglioli	56
Potato Pancakes	96
Pumpkin Bread	25
Pumpkin-Apple Muffins	23
Red Lentil Stew	99
Roasted Garlic Mashed Potatoes	127
Roasted Potato Wedges	128
Sherry's Peas and Carrots	124
Spaghetti Puttanesca	101
Spaghetti Squash and Tomatoes	136
Spanakopita	72
Spanish Rice	90
Spicy Red Beans and Rice	113
Spinach Bread	144
Stuffed Peppers	88
Stuffed Potatoes	133
Sundried Tomato Pasta	69
Sweet Potato Fries	129
Tabouli	48
Tangy Vegetable Stew	107
Uncandied Sweet Potatoes	132
Vegetarian Chili	83
Vegetarian Chili with Bulgur Wheat	103
Winter Vegetable Soup	54

Yummy Fried Potatoes 126
Zucchini Bread 24

Category C--Concentrated Proteins

Breakfast Fritatta	16
Broccoli & Swiss Cheese Quiche	70
Cod with Dill Sauce	110
Delicious Panfried Fish	87
Eggplant Lasagna	115
Feta and Tomato Shrimp Scampi	108
Irish Cream	149
Salmon with Brown Sugar Glaze	92
Salmon with Horseradish Sauce	98
Salmon with Raspberry Sauce	111
Sea Bass with Feta	112
Seafood Stew	105
Shrimp Scampi	91
Shrimp with Basil-Garlic Sauce	97
Spinach & Feta Cheese Quiche	71

Desserts

Black Magic Cake	164
Chocolate Custard Pie	156
Congo Bars	155
Dutch Apple Pie	153
Eggnog	143
Mike's Favorite Pecan Pie	158
Raspberry Bars	160
Sweet Potato Pie	159

The Best Brownies Ever   161
The World's Best Carrot Cake   162
Traditional Apple Pie   154
Vodka Punch   148